Discovering
YOU
in
You

Your Way to
Health and Happiness

Brian R. Clement, Ph.D.

Katherine C. Powell Ed.D.

PUBLISHED BY TriMark PRESS, INC., DEERFIELD BEACH, FLORIDA.

LIBRARY OF CONGRESS CATALOGING-IN-PUBLICATION DATA
DISCOVERING YOU IN YOU
BRIAN R. CLEMENT, PH.D.
KATHERINE C. POWELL, ED.D.

P. CM.
ISBN: 978-1-943401-97-0
LIBRARY OF CONGRESS CONTROL NUMBER: 2022907456

E-22
10 9 8 7 6 5 4 3 2 1
FIRST EDITION
PRINTED AND BOUND IN THE UNITED STATES OF AMERICA

A PUBLICATION OF TriMark PRESS, INC.
368 SOUTH MILITARY TRAIL
DEERFIELD BEACH, FL 33442
800.889.0693

WWW.TRIMARKPRESS.COM

ACKNOWLEDGMENTS

Discovering YOU in You is a product of over fifty years of the authors' experiences and contributions from the Hippocrates Health Institute (HHI) staff and guests. The authors, Dr. Brian Clement and Dr. Katherine Powell, gratefully acknowledge the talented and gifted people who have told their stories and who have participated in HHI's health and healing educational process. We thank the executive administrators led by Susan Maharaj and Blake Clement for their creative ideas and computer talents, with Dr. Catherine Boyle's assistance. The authors appreciate their insightful editing skills that helped create and produce our offering for you.

Teachers learn from their students also and the HHI Health Educational Center is a prime example of ongoing valuable interchange of experience and information for all participants. We would like to thank Josh Weinberger (attended Yale University and worked at The New Yorker magazine) for his creative editing skills, genius, and multi-talented writing ideas. We also thank Raymond F. Wells (BA in Psychology/History from Dakota Wesleyan University) for capturing the amazing nature photos that portray our message.

We thank our friends and family who support us on a daily basis and who contribute to our happiness. There is much pride in our children and grandchildren who keep the beacon of light glowing for future generations. We also thank our publishers for making it possible to share this book, our gift to you, which represents our knowledge, experience, and expertise. We thank you for your time in reading what will hopefully help you on your journey for health and happiness.

Table of Contents

REALITY   PATH

"Learn from yesterday, live for today, and hope for the future... Imagination is more important than knowledge. For knowledge is limited, whereas imagination embraces the entire world, stimulating progress, giving birth to evolution."

ఌ Albert Einstein

*D*iscovering *YOU in You* is a comprehensive and complete guide to a life journey of self-discovery. The path of finding you through your many outer layers can be challenging. We provide experience, practical stories, and educational information based on research and professionals' findings. Your goals in life should be to

Introduction

discover yourself and harmonize your mind/body connection. Your thoughts and emotions are energy directed by the power of self, will, and healthy practices.

Our ancient teachers were the Stoics, a school of philosophy founded in the third century B.C. A well-known Stoic was Marcus Aurelius, Emperor of Rome, whose Greek teacher Epictetus said, "There is only one way to happiness, and that is to cease worrying about things which are beyond the power of our will." Stoics believed that we had to be the best we can be and share it with others.

When discovering the core of YOU, all obstacles will fall aside and YOU will emerge with a life worth living through living food and a healthy lifestyle. This process is only activated when you are open to the possibility of change. This adventure will help you find the YOU hidden inside. Discovering yourself elevates you to a new plateau of liberation.

The book contains three themes:

HEALTH (Self-awareness, food, and choices)

HAPPINESS (A creative, fulfilling, and happy lifestyle)

INTERACTIONS (Connections to self, others and environment)

Discovering YOU in You is a gathering of proven methods and advanced science that has helped hundreds of thousands prevent premature aging and disease. There have been endless reports of people who have reversed even the most catastrophic illnesses by healing their relationships with self and others. They elevated their health to an exceptional level that in turn manifested the happiness that they sought their entire life.

Each section is told in a story format by the authors and colleagues, so that it becomes more personalized and the experiences can then be clearly depicted and relatable. We are made of energy and vibrations which surround us, the world, and all people and things that we connect to. We need personal harmony with ourselves to continue our positive flow congruent with all else. Consciousness will provoke honest and true bonds with everyone that we touch. We all seek creative, balanced, healthy and joyous futures.

Health is happiness and happiness is health. Without this all else fails and our joy is diminished. Your criteria to meet personal goals requires pure honesty, integrity, and unblemished will. Additionally, your intention must be concrete and accompanied by openness and a desire to feel at peace. You can easily achieve this once you recognize and release your potential. When your well-being is established, the wealth and wisdom of eternity is now manifested in your every action. Faith, courage, hope and the relinquishing of fear are the hallmarks to emotional and spiritual grace. Being honest with yourself is the key to the figurative door of eternal elation.

We all have gifts and talents. Our job is to find them and share them with others. When we are healthy, we find the wealth of joy within us, then we glow with positivity. To achieve our goals we need faith, courage, hope, and to live without fear, anxiety, or worry, since each negative emotion can hold us back. If we are not honest with ourselves, we will wander into darkness.

A well-known, accomplished, and brilliant MD is Dr. Tara Levine, an integrative physician, who follows her heart maintaining her professional calling. She received several humanitarian, and compassionate service awards which are notable and quite unique for a doctor. She joins an elite group of health professionals that have raised the bar in the current disconnected state of medicine.

Her gift of relating to the holistic and total person, (physical, emotional, mental, and spiritual) contributes to her advocacy of healthy food, exercise, and good relations to keep a balanced lifestyle. Dr. Levine's insights reflect our three themes: Health, Happiness, and Interactions. When immersing yourself in total health, abundant happiness, and stable relationships, the hidden self will emerge.

Introduction

Dr. Tara Levine relates her story:

As an Internal Medicine physician, I, Dr. Tara Levine, have a unique perspective on health and wellness. I have studied every organ system and understand their function. I also have an in depth knowledge about the aspects of healthy living, as I mostly care for geriatrics patients in my practice. Over the years in speaking to patients every day, I have learned some pearls of wisdom regarding longevity and aging gracefully. In medicine, we gather information by looking at proven clinical research in peer reviewed journals and gain insight by collaboration with other medical professionals. By combining my medical knowledge with my perceptions, I have reflected on the most effective blueprint of health and wellness. There is no guaranteed path to health and happiness for all people. There is no prescription that can be written for this. There are multiple ways to achieve this formula to improve your health and create a meaningful life. I tell my patients there are several modalities to stack the odds in your favor for living a long, healthy life free of disease.

Statistically the number one cause of death in the developed world is heart disease. The major risk factors that can contribute to heart disease are smoking, diabetes, hypertension and high cholesterol, as well as family history. Other predictors include obesity, sedentary lifestyle, and stress. Sugar consumption is the foremost nemesis for overall health. Not only does it provoke blood sugar concerns, but forges a trail for dementia, cancer, viral and bacterial disease. It is of paramount importance to control your sugar if you are a diabetic, as well as controlling your cholesterol and blood pressure. Lifestyle modifications including diet, exercise, and stress management, have proven to be antidotes to the major killers. Proper nutrition, a diet rich in vegetables, whole grains and fruit are a good foundation to help prevent heart disease and cancer.

There is a profound proverb: "the body heals with play, the mind heals with laughter, and the spirit heals with joy". There is no doubt that the author of this inspiring reflection was spot on. This notion that the mind, body and spirit are the triune of humanity, requires a fourth dimension which is inclusive interaction.

Sleep is a central contributor to health or disorder. More than half the population now state they do not sleep adequately. Drugs and alcohol are problematic since they are deeply damaging to our health. More time is lost at work and more accidents occur on highways globally when people do not experience the uninterrupted REM rest required.

Exercise gives you more energy and can release endorphins to enhance your positive mood. Healthy, affirmative interactions accompany good health. The most comprehensive study ever done on centenarians and super centenarians. "the New England Centenarian Study," has now added relationships as a core factor in the length of lifespan.

We can also boost our well-being by unplugging from technology, getting outside where there are no computers, televisions, tablets or phone screens. Technology, with all of its advantages, presents the foremost schism in human relationships. People's focus is on a screen for hours a day. Young people sitting next to one another are engaged in texting rather than interaction. Major universities, like Colombia, had to offer a course on human communication without computers, which was mandatory for all freshman. Now, when we require more touch, expression, and greater interaction than ever, we have diminished it to an afterthought. Additionally, we have been warned that using social media platforms, such as ZOOM, make us vulnerable to cyber hacking. Our future is questionable since clarity in relationships manifest peace, harmony, and success but our current technological mode increases the opportunity for misinterpretations.

When partners do not speak and listen, it is surely the end of the relationship. When nations become isolationists and do not interact with other countries, it precipitates misunderstandings and even war. When coworkers do not communicate, cultures are sabotaged. All of our physical and emotional disorders stem from feeling disconnected. All meaning and purpose requires acknowledgment from others. Aggressive tendencies can hinder our relationships. Releasing aggression and tension in a positive way through exercise helps to hormonally neutralize stress, and relieve anxiety.

Brigham and Young University conducted a long-term study on loneliness. This is pertinent since more than half the populations endures this sad place. After years of feeling alone, people literally pass on fifteen years sooner than the general population. This is equal to long-term smokers.

People with strong and broad social relationships are happier, healthier and live longer. Close relationships with family and friends provide love, meaning, support and feelings of self-worth. Broader networks bring a sense of belonging, such as religion or organizations. Taking action to strengthen our relationships and create new connections is essential for happiness. If you treasure your interactions, make the effort to express your feelings. Putting yourself out there to meet people and making yourself vulnerable can be difficult; however, it can ultimately lead to love. That love leads to compassion towards others. It is fundamentally important to show your compassion outwardly.

Caring about others and building significant connections are keys to fulfillment. Helping other people is not only good for them and an altruistic thing to do; it also makes us happy. It appears that the old adage "it is better to give than to receive" might have some scientific support. Giving creates stronger connections between people and helps to build a happier environment.

It is not always about money. We can lend our time, ideas and energy into helping others. Holding a door open for someone, saying bless you upon someone sneezing and paying it forward, can help spread kindness. But foremost, treating yourself well is of the utmost importance because no one else is going to do it. Stick to your values and do not become easily swayed.

People who have meaning and purpose in their lives are happier, feel more in control and get more out of what they do. Where do we find meaning and purpose? Perhaps it may be through religious faith, being a parent or doing a job that makes a difference. The answers vary for each of us, but they all involve being connected to something bigger than ourselves. Inspiration exposes us to new ideas and helps us stay curious and engaged. It also gives us a strong sense of self via accomplishment and helps boost our self-confidence and resilience. There are many ways to learn new things – not just through formal qualifications. We can share skills with friends, join a club, play sports and so much more. Venturing outside of your comfort zone in order to try new experiences brings excitement and a sense of accomplishment. Set realistic goals for yourself. Feeling good about the future is important for happiness. We all need goals to motivate us and these need to be challenging enough to excite us, but also are achievable.

Therefore, manage your time effectively. If we try to attempt the impossible, this brings unnecessary stress. Do not complain. Only you are responsible for yourself. When you make a conscious decision to do something, you will be prepared to bear whatever consequences come with it. If you want something, you must work hard to earn it. This is why I chose a professional degree because I did not want to have to rely on anyone for income. Don't expect anyone to do anything for you. If they do, it is a privilege, not an entitlement. Don't rely on anyone for happiness, as you may inevitably be let down.

Choosing ambitious and practical goals gives our lives direction, and brings a sense of accomplishment and satisfaction when we achieve them. Finding resilience is a key. All of us have times of stress, loss, failure or trauma. But how we respond has a big impact on our well-being. We often cannot choose what happens to us, but we can form our attitude towards situations. In practice, it's not always easy; however, one of the most exciting findings from recent research is that resilience, like many other life skills, can be learned. In life, there are setbacks and bumps in the road; it is how you handle these challenges that define the type of person you will become. Do not worry about situations, things or people that are out of your control. Your response is what you can control. It is how you deal with dysfunction that can help mold you into a successful person. Staying positive and optimistic is paramount. Positive emotions - like joy, gratitude, contentment, inspiration, and pride enrich your life creating the passionate existence that you've always sought to live.

As Dr. Tara Levine has cited, what matters is mental, physical, and emotional health. When we fill the mind with valid, positive, and healthy intentions, as well as concise spiritual missions, there is no room for self-sabotage or for depressing thoughts. These concepts are simple guidelines for our work, home, and leisure. Consciousness and courage keep us on our paths to fulfill our goals. A healthy lifestyle approach works for individuals who are awakened. They need to understand their weaknesses, strengths, and wants by being more aware that only they can take care of themselves. Once achieved, the road to wellness and happiness is a continuous journey of wonder and joy. A key component is food. Food is fuel and must contain: Nutrients, Hormones, Oxygen, Phytochemicals, and Enzymes. These are locked into the cells of unprocessed and uncooked organic edible plants.

Over time we have harvested knowledge establishing seven pillars of wellness. Each and every pillar offers a clear and concise directive to achieving harmony. The voyage of *Discovering YOU in You* will be aided by these pillars:

The 7 Pillars

1. UNDERSTAND YOURSELF — involves self-realization which creates a life worth living. This begins with an honest self-evaluation to set goals for self-actualization. Once true honesty is at work, who you really are and your motives will come forward.

2. ENHANCE IMAGINATION — involves your visualization as it slowly becomes your reality. Imagination is the most important talent you possess, since it can let you create the life that you ultimately need to become healthy and happy. See who you are.

3. EXPRESS YOURSELF — involves sharing your personal passions and growing through your commitment to achieving them. Without desires, and passion to complete your desires, motivation does not exist. You cannot create when you do not challenge yourself.

4. SHIELD YOURSELF — involves not being fearful of experiences and events, but rather from avoiding energy-draining activities, people, places and things. Be aware of people and activities that drain energy and leave you unable to be clear or creative.

5. EXPAND YOURSELF — involves immersing yourself in life enhancing food, music, movement, art, nature, etc. When becoming one with the beauty of creation, you can manifest an extraordinary life. As you become aware, this is within your grasp.

6. CHALLENGE YOURSELF — involves always wanting to aspire to do your best by reaching your desired plateau. You need to grow through acquiring new knowl-

edge, life experiences and accepting new challenges. No one wants to be bored.

7. EXTEND YOUR LIFE — involves living at a pinnacle level of commitment where you are perpetually fulfilled. At this level you will be providing the fuel and focus to have a longer, creative, and productive life to share with others. You are living a fulfilled life.

Your body and mind function optimally when they are nourished, exercised, hydrated, and rested. This is the description of health. Abominable behaviors are represented by self-sabotage. Although self-damaging behavior can be learned, once you have the courage to put your health "first" and ultimately learn to overcome adversities, you will find your true self. Diet, exercise, and rest patterns either denigrate your body or build it into a well-functioning partner.

As we grow happier with every accomplishment, we are creating a map that leads us to embrace ourselves. We gain self-confidence with each accomplished task. If we build self-esteem by feeling we deserve to be happy, we then also increase an ever expanding healthy existence. We can live for the moment, without fear, anxieties, worries, or other cloudy thoughts that take over our brain and diminish clear thinking. The more satisfied we feel, the more we will continue our progress to maintain health.

Discovering YOU in You will guide you on your life's journey to health, happiness, and more satisfying social interactions.

Section I
HEALTH

HARMONIOUS WELL-BEING

SELF   REFLECTION

"If we could give every individual the right amount of nourishment and exercise, not too little and not too much, we would have found the safest way to health...Natural forces within us are the true healers of disease...Walking is man's best medicine."

ᑐ **Hippocrates**

*T*o reach harmonious well-being, the first step is awareness. As we continue our wellness quest, we are discovering who we are as individuals. The food choices we make depict our level of health. Acquiring health is our most important goal, since whatever we do affects our well-being and our ability to feel confident in all our endeavors. We have to maintain our physical health via the choices and decisions we make; however, these decisions will also impact our personalities, emotions, and behaviors. It is very important to be honest with ourselves and to understand what we need to be healthy. Awareness is required to prevent jeopardizing our core essence.

We are constantly making decisions concerning our bodies every minute of the day. We need to eat healthfully, exercise, have a stable or calm attitude, and be open to learn and understand new knowledge. Ignorance is the enemy. When we develop as individuals, we accept the responsibility of taking care of ourselves. If we are unhappy or depressed, we won't be able to do that successfully. We can't afford to become complacent and satisfied with mediocrity. No one else can really take care of us; the onus is ours. We have the burden, since we know our truth; thus we can't lie, hide, or become shallow. Honesty is our only salvation. This Hippocrates Health Institute (HHI) book, *Discovering YOU in You*, depicts health topics reviewed from Hippocrates Institutes' historic contributions. This health theme has many facets as demonstrated in these behaviors:

1. AWARENESS — being cognizant of what is happening or why is key to being aware. We are challenged to not ignore our ill-at-ease signs and given our proclivity for demise, we can, without awareness, be killing ourselves slowly with our decisions and choices. As benign as these signs may seem we need to dig deeper to make sure we are on a healthy path. We do this, if we are open and able to listen to ourselves honestly.

The HHI book associated with this theme is *Food is Medicine* (Vol.1), since this book is a complete and comprehensive guide. Choosing food as medicine was taught by the philosopher and physician, Hippocrates, fifth century BC. Important data and research-based articles substantiate the pertinent findings as described for a healthy body, mind, and spirit.

2. INDIVIDUALITY — allowing differences in personality is important since no two people are the same but can share mutual findings and experiences. Understanding the scientific background or evidence of why food is medicine assists in each person's quest for the correct path to health and wellness. We respect each person's uniqueness.

    The HHI book associated with this theme is *Food is Medicine* (Vol. 2), since this book shows studies summarized on the efficacy of foods such as, sprouts, garlic, mushrooms, etc. that can assist in our healing. Each person has special needs and will choose what is appropriate for their health benefit. The food analysis is comprehensive and easily understood.

3. CONSCIOUSNESS — knowing the mind's ultimate potential is to be awakened. This helps us remember and acknowledge its infinite power. Decision-making is a product of a conscious mind at work without other disturbances to cloud clear thinking. This book helps us understand that medicine comes from the food we eat. Plants are vital to us.

    The HHI book associated with this theme is *Food is Medicine* (Vol. 3), since this volume outlines many articles that substantiate plant food as our essential source for health and wellness. Listing the variety of plant-based foods and their healing properties gives us a potpourri of choices for our own individual needs. The more we understand what exists the more we can choose wisely.

4. CHOICES — making decisions depends on understanding the options involved and identifying what we deem as important for well-being. Our culture has constantly changed the parameters for valid and safe food selection; therefore,

the choice is ours. For example, there are currently many other substitutes rather than dairy which are wiser selections.

The HHI book associated with this theme is *Dairy Deception*, since what we have learned about dairy keeps changing and the truth is finally revealed. Deception is a word that tells us that what we hear or read may not be the truth and our job is to find out the truth through our own research.   Our endeavors need to assuage illnesses from dairy products. Science is finally acknowledging this.

5. EXPERIENCES — learning from our mistakes is important since it highlights what our next steps need to be to get it right. We evolve based on our learned experiences, background, and personality. With the correct knowledge we can choose healthy viable supplements rather than what is sold as healthy. The challenges and rewards are ours.

The HHI book associated with this theme is *Supplements Exposed*. There is an ever growing chorus pursuing the demise of our ignorance. As long as we can recognize truth and differentiate from lies we can add to our knowledge base through valid experiences. We can associate our new learning with the old by being able to adjust appropriate information and discard invalid theories.

6. OPENNESS — seeing what is missing in our lives life is a sign of maturity. We need to be willing to see the truth to make decisions with knowledge and facts. Being open means to have the ability to see clearly without blinders and obstacles which prevents new learning from seeping into our brains and awareness. Life should be simple.

The HHI book associated with this theme is *Killer Fish,* since we all are finally aware of the problems with pollution in the ocean and the effects on our health from both farm and wild fish. We are now open to learning the truth about our oceans and our history of neglect. The responsibility is within us to accept the truth and help others see it.

7. REALIZATION — living awake with understanding and knowledge is a prerequisite for intelligent choices and the realization of the differences that are available. We can only begin to understand our earthly plight when we realize that the best food for us is from the earth in a natural and humane method of delivery for ingestion.

The HHI book associated with this theme is *Poison Poultry,* since the knowledge is finally exposed to the cruel and inhuman treatment of poultry. The poisons they are fed and exposed to is inside the poultry slaughtered for our consumption. The task is simple. Either we are awake and aware or asleep and ignorant. We can only choose truth for health.

Personality Development

For centuries researchers have been observing our population to identify different types of personalities and one test that has survived through much scrutiny is called "THE BIG FIVE." There is a positive premise and a negative aspect for each type of personality. Since there is a wide spectrum between each category, people can be somewhere in the middle depending on the situation. THE BIG FIVE are:

1. Openness — being open for learning and free versus closed off and ignorant,

2. Conscientiousness — being disciplined and organized versus disorganized,

3. Extroverted — being outgoing and social versus introverted and isolated,

4. Agreeableness — being friendly and kind versus angry and disagreeable,

5. Neuroticism — being anxious and worried versus calm and peaceful.

Many people have a combination of both positive and negative personality aspects depending on their genetics, background, or experiences. Others can be predominant in one or two types. These can change throughout the individual's lifetime; however, people need to be aware of their dominant personalities. Differences are what make us unique. An awareness of the qualities that we possess can help us through stress and difficult hardships throughout our development. Accepting who we are is the key to health and happiness, since we can only change what we know. Personalities affect our behavior in various situations. Understanding who we are can lead to new adventures as we continue our path of self-discovery.

A stable or balanced personality, including all parts of self (physical, emotional, and mental), is a prerequisite for a healthy person. Life is difficult at times and without health, it becomes even more daunting. To become healthy means to take care of ourselves and not overindulge in anything that causes illness or disease. Honesty is the key for this process to be successful.

A goal of adolescence and young adults is to develop high self-esteem and their own belief system separate from their parents. Intimacy develops through marriage or friendships; thus, feelings of not belonging and loneliness will not prevail. During old age or upon departing this world, we either have no regrets or feel despair. This is the time when life is reviewed, legacy is considered, gratitude is established, and time with loved ones is special.

Personality development is important since the development of competence, self-esteem, confidence, and self-identity in each individual is established. As we evolve, we are able to make healthy decisions in life rather than dwell in mistrust, lost hope, or fear. By overcoming each psychosocial crisis in our experiences, we develop a unique personality that helps us make valid and correct decisions for health, happiness and well-being.

The environment can also affect our personality and behavior and vice versa. Living free of toxins and air pollutants is essential for our spiritual and physical well-being. Becoming dehydrated can cause dangerous health issues; thus we need to be aware of drinking pure water that is half our body weight in ounces daily. If we keep ourselves in a harmonious environment with adequate fuel, we are winning.

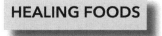

HEALING FOODS

Three Volumes on Healthy Food

The three HHI books that comprise the series, *Food is Medicine*, are by far the most comprehensive books and teaching guides of their kind, created by the world's number one lifestyle medical center and foremost authority in raw and living foods nutrition, now known as Hippocrates Wellness. Volume 1 of Food is Medicine discusses the scientific evidence behind many common diseases. Volume 2 discusses edible plant foods, fruits and spices from A-Z. Volume 3 specifically addresses foods that undermine health. There is endless research and evidence of the healing properties of food for health issues.

The *Food Is Medicine* series (Volumes 1, 11, and 111) are a contribution to the field of healthcare in the most critical area of nutrition: healing. Over the last half century, healthcare has primarily been based on assisting those in the grips of disease and premature aging. At Hippocrates Health Institute, we teach that the core tool facilitating this critical issue is raw food nutrition. There is a general consensus even among those who know little about the subject that the more fruits and vegetables we eat, the healthier we will be. And further still, the greener the better. HHI developed these three volumes (Food is Medicine) as the foundation for its Health Institute and educational programs.

Food Is Medicine (Vol. 1) - Awareness

"Health is the greatest gift, contentment the greatest wealth, faithfulness the best relationship. To keep the body in good health is a duty ... otherwise we shall not be able to keep our minds strong and clear. All the money in the world can't buy you back good health."

ᴄᴏ *Buddha*

Inherent in individual growth is personal awareness. Without consciousness we cannot understand ourselves or make wise food choices. If you are one of the millions of people who have learned about the superior health and nutritional benefits of raw and living foods and want to begin experiencing their life-enhancing qualities now, then Food is Medicine is for you.

In 1948, a research scientist identified elements in his microscope that were neutralizing microbes and mutagens. These eventually became what we today call Phytochemicals. The National Institute of

Health in the USA elevated interest in the area of Phytochemicals in the 1980s and gave birth to the most important findings in the history of nutritional science. Now, and for more than five decades, there has been endless research conducted into these magical nutrients that literally search out and destroy every disorder known to man.

There is almost a mystical overtone surrounding this story, since plants were on this earth hundreds of millions of years before our species arrived. Somehow there were chemical programs placed in the cells of these botanicals that would selectively target human maladies depending upon the vegetable, fruit or the family of plants they came from. The nature of plants is truly remarkable. As widely discussed, everything from anti-aging to anti-tuberculosis can be addressed via the consumption of these plant-based foods.

Scientifically we've established, in the last two generations, the synergistic effect of certain nutrients. If one is good we now know that two, three or more together may be better. Amazingly, by mixing the natural chemistries of foods and herbs it amplifies the medicinal benefits.

Dr. Brian expresses his knowledge about nutrients in healthy foods below:

Nutritionists often get in the rhythm of telling everyone that everything has to do with the food they eat. And deeper still, looking at how much you eat and at what time of day you consume your fare. Today, mainstream speaks about intermittent fasting, which is just reflective of how we all formerly ate. Fasting, which has been part of every culture throughout history, was understood to be part of a natural lifestyle. Hundreds of studies by renowned University Research Centers have shown that longer life and reduced potential for disease is a result of eating less. Before choosing to eat less, reflect on it. What we do eat has to be highly nutritious, unprocessed, and as much as possible, uncooked foods. From Parkinson's to Alzheimer's disease symptoms and their progression have clinically improved and in some cases have been reversed by following these natural dietary restrictions.

We share the planet earth with at least 8 million other species. Every species in nature thrive on 100 percent raw food diet. Ours is the only group that chose to cook, process, radiate, and chemicalize what we ingest. For this reason we are the sickest of all species, both physically and emotionally. There is a plethora of global research on the nutritional destruction that occurs when we process and heat food. As a matter of fact, even organic vegetables and plants that are highly heated categorically become noted carcinogens. Leukocytosis is when the immune system attacks the highly heated food compromising the very cells that protect you from diseases.

All natural foods and certainly others have oil, however once heated, they have been known to help create heart disease and cancer for more than six decades. And lastly acrylamides, from highly heated carbohydrates have been directly linked to the creation of a wide variety of cancers. Many scientists often throw out the challenge that there is not enough research. This is the furthest thing from the truth. Not only do we write in elaborate detail about sicknesses coming from cooked and processed food, but also some of the world's respected scientists have dedicated their lives to this critical subject.

How we have ever allowed our fields to be sprayed with pesticides, fungicides, and herbicides is beyond belief. To compound this problem, there have been scientists and even Universities that have fraudulently led the public to believe that although this kills insects and animals, somehow it does not affect humans. Most people casually eat non-organic choices and these poisons collect in cells which cause disease.

We know that food is medicine, not only for the body, but also for the soul. Each and every one of us must rethink our relationship with what we ingest. Noted author, Colin Campbell once said, "The most intimate act we will ever have is with the very food we consume." You can see that malnourishment and ultimately death occurs when we consume nothing. Does it not make sense to you that we slowly die when we lack essential nutrients?

You may ask, where do I begin? To start, you must gravitate toward a fresh, organic, vegan diet. How quickly depends upon the level of challenge that you face. Here at the Hippocrates Wellness Center half the population attends to prevent aging and disease while the other half to prevent further progression of illness or demise. Obviously the latter has to immediately embrace the necessary dietary shift. Others may take six months to a year at their own pace, becoming increasingly familiar with the new food choices. Olympic gold medalists and people fighting catastrophic disease interestingly require the maximum nutrient choice. Top athletes have described greater endurance, strength, and less injury once they are fueled by living plant- based food.

Although there are hundreds of choices for anti-aging supplementation, be assured the most effective is the consumption of living foods. Viable antioxidants, easy to digest proteins, essential fats, vitamins, and minerals and yes, Phytochemicals, are naturally occurring and originate from these delectable botanicals. There is never a time that a person should ever consider eating anything other than from the table of nature since there is never a bad meal. Awareness is the key in choosing healthy food and to assure a vital and energetic lifestyle. Self-reflection guides us to keep on target.

Food Is Medicine (Vol. 2) - Individuality

*"It is health that is real wealth, and not pieces of gold and silver...
The future depends on what we do in the present...Where there is
love, there is life...He who has hope has health and he who has hope,
has everything." (Arabian Proverb)"*

ભ **Gandhi**

As we discover ourselves, we begin to develop individuality and
eventually we can enhance our imagination. We can now understand
who we are and our purpose on this planet. With all of our species'
scientific developments and phenomenal inventions, we have somehow estranged ourselves from the very planet on which we reside.
Mindlessly, we have forged ahead in the field of "healthcare" to find
the latest and greatest "cure." All of the medicines that the major pharmaceuticals develop or try and replicate, and greatly profit from, originate from plants or rocks.

Why is it we have not spent time, money, and effort on delving
deeply into the phenomenal world of plant cells? Out time is spent
on reinventing the wheel rather than learning how to re-attach it and
move forward. Evolution of our species did not occur in a vacuum
and all life forms, including the very food we eat, provide nutrition
and equally medicine.

One of the great findings of our time, penicillin, actually came
out of a food, yet we have synthesized antibiotics to such a high level that its origins are vaguely present. Many of the common fruits
and vegetables, herbs and spices that we've consumed throughout our
lives harbor powerful, medicinal properties.

"An apple a day keeps the doctor away", was a rhyme we learned
as a child. But today we have scientific research that shows it helps to
slow aging, Alzheimer's disease, cardiovascular disease, and muscle
injury, plus two-dozen other disorders.

Allopathic physicians are not trained in medical schools to know this, but rather have been guided to be proficient in writing prescriptions. There is no doubt that most women and men in the field of medicine would love to possess knowledge on food-based methods to help their patients. When reading the data on curcumin, an extract from turmeric, the only thing it doesn't help us do is walk on water. Garlic, which has always been considered a seasoning, is a well-researched and proven antibacterial, antiviral, and anticancer food/herb.

Lemon and lime were first used as medicine by a Scottish admiral in the British navy during the mid-eighteenth century. Scurvy was a formidable killer of sailors globally. As a matter of fact, on long voyages, it was anticipated that half the men would die, most often from this disease. This admiral noticed that when ships visited tropical ports and the men consumed citrus, the death rate plummeted. He correctly speculated that limes have some magical potion in them to avert death. He began arming all marine craft with baskets of this citrus fruit. His discovery helped establish the British empire.

When the sailors came ashore the gentle fragrance of limes permeated the air giving the Brits the nick name "Limeys." Centuries later we discovered that limes are high in Vitamin C. Beriberi was a nutritional deficiency (Vitamin B1 or thiamine) that killed thousands of people. All too often cerebral scientists over think solutions and do not respect the simplicity of achieving correct remedies in an effortless way.

As children we are often told to eat our spinach, while men with prostrate problems, men and woman with rectal or stomach concerns, and even breast, cervical and colon cancer should all take heed. There is significant evidence for all of this plus much more. Today's modern plague of cancer, which over half the population will contract some form of during their lifetime, should know the top ten cancer fighting foods based on cancer type prevention or treatments.

Here are the Top 10 cancer fighting foods:

1. Garlic – 15 types of cancers are attacked by the medicine of this superior food

2. Curcumin – aids in the depletion of 14 types of cancer

3. Cranberries – aids in 13 types

4. Broccoli and their sprouts – aids in 11 types

5. Medicine mushrooms – aids in 11 types

6. Resveratrol – aids in 10 types

7. Spinach – aids in 9 types

8. Most berries – aids in 8 types

9. Sunflower Sprouts – aids in 7 types

10. Tomatoes – aids in 9 types

Many selections are geographically unique and ethnic in their history. In the west, it's rare that algae is consumed. Whereas on the contrary, for Asians, some Africans, specifically in Chad, people on the coast of Donegal Ireland, and in Northern Maine, and Nova Scotia, these are commonplace delicacies.

Being the very first life form that literally created oxygen on this planet, it's needless to say algae contain a plethora of beneficial elements and we are sure there are some that we have not yet discovered. Algae/sea vegetables have been positively correlated with allergies, immune system health, dementia, pneumonia, tuberculosis and about thirty-eight other maladies. Today's emerging science in the botanical arena has advanced our understanding of the fundamental need that we have in scientifically documenting the powers locked within nature.

Dr. Anna Maria Clement, co-founder of HHI, expresses her concern for our environment and future in this interview with a guest:

There is a history that we should have learned from and there are thousands of generations that were never exposed to the disease-causing manmade chemistry that we have to endure today. These inorganic molecules mutate our cells and wreak havoc with our immune system. Life is always about choices. We have to find a way to create health, happiness, and healing.

Governments and corporations care more for profits and less about human life. For this reason, we have to fight the good fight. Apathy doesn't work. I have never before heard the expression "living food" before; I thought all food was dead or I wouldn't have eaten it. I never thought of that until I was at Hippocrates and it now makes complete sense to me having experienced how positively my body reacts to it.

In conclusion, I am optimistic that we humans will find a way to turn the tide and begin embracing pro-body and pro-earth practices. Together, we all can make change occur, via knowledge, commitment, conviction, and love.

There is a silent yet powerful revolution that will elevate humanities ability to prevent and reverse aging and disease. This will be a combination of plants, genes, and electromagnetic frequencies, all of which are the basis of life as we know it. The merry-go-round will soon halt and we will get off on solid ground that is based on natural history, quantum biology, and physics and energy medicine. These are not separate, but woven together by the very fact that all life forms contain each of these powerful agents. You often hear the term, super food, thrown around mostly as a sales pitch; however, these foods are truly superior.

Here are the foods important for healing along with the number of conditions they assist, based on science:

1. Algae – 44
2. Garlic – 23

3. Curcumin – 29
4. Grapes and Berries – 23
5. Onions – 20
6. Apples – 19
7. Blueberries – 19
8. Cranberries – 17
9. Pomegranate –16
10. Strawberries –15

We strongly advise that public medicine add a new section to include "foods that heal" and "foods that prevent." We highly encourage each of you to open your hearts and minds to the enormity of medicinal properties that proper foods contain. By leaving behind the death and dying cuisine and embracing this life-filled fare, you will take a leap so extraordinary that you may just become younger and stronger.

Food Is Medicine (Vol. 3) – Consciousness

"It is easy to hate and it is difficult to love. This is how the whole scheme of things works. All good things are difficult to achieve, and bad things are very easy to get...Everyone eats and drinks; yet only few appreciate the taste of food...Food for the body is not enough, there must be food for the soul."

ᴥ Confucius

We can begin to appreciate the vast knowledge we need to digest in order to make conscious decisions about our food intake. This process includes our need to express ourselves and is a fundamental pillar of health. Our clarity begins with whole healthy food to expand our knowledge. Every day we make choices. Our ability to be in the present moment is vital. Stress and anxiety appear when we are not awake or conscious of our actions. The onus of living a mindful and healthy life is ours. Our well-being depends on our ability to recognize our health needs.

International food producers and their industry promoters have been selling us a bill of goods for more than a century. As our health declines, and science progresses, we recognize that practically everything we were told that was good for us is actually the opposite. Meat, the flesh from a wide variety of animals, has been touted as a great source of protein. In fact, when one consumes flesh, it is like eating second hand food since all of the amino acids (protein) that are contained in their organs and muscles come from plants. All meats contain three acids that erode bones and cells and leave behind saturated fat that clog veins, capillaries, and organs. When we speak of meat, this includes red meat, pork, poultry, fish and wild game.

There are volumes of evidence substantiating how eating the traditional fare of meat and dairy create everything from acne to strokes and the risk increases as years pass. Brain washing has been so effective that most people are frightened to move beyond the meat-myth and begin consuming what the young, bright, and best athletes have now embraced. Luckily what we have been teaching for decades regarding implementing a plant-based diet for optimal health, is making its way into mainstream lifestyles. Many plant-based superstars such as actors, CEOs, athletes, and laymen are abundantly functional and healthy.

It's not bad enough we chew and swallow clumps of flesh, but we often wash it down with secretions from other animals called milk. By law, a glass of milk is permitted to have 750,000 puss spores in it. Further, it's not bad enough that we drink such unclean and unnatural fluid, but they now also make a wide variety of products from it. We are overwhelmed with choices such as yogurt, kefir, butter, cheese, whip cream, ice cream, and other dairy products.

Each of these "foods" has much higher amounts of bacteria and gather far more of the heavy metals, chemicals, and poisons that are in the animals secretions. This is why science has outed the industry and disproven the health benefits that they've sold the public. Everything from allergies and asthma to mental illness has been connected to dairy food consumption.

Brian and Anna Maria relate one of their guest experiences:

In 2008, a middle-aged woman from Quebec, Canada, arrived at HHI with three tumors in her abdomen. She, like most others, was told that she would have to live with them or have them surgically removed with a high chance of them re-growing. Her choice was to let natural-approaches-to-life assist her ill body to regain balance. As we have seen so often over the years here at Hippocrates, she was able to diminish the tumors and place the disorder in full remission by loving herself enough to follow our advice and protocol. Getting to know her, we found out she has a loving, committed relationship with her husband who was incessantly supportive. During her stay he called every day to see her progress. This sense of loving support was paramount to her recovery.

Independently we require a concrete self-evaluation that fuels utter confidence and complete conviction. This does not mean that we do not need others or that we can't further enhance our level of joy by lovingly sharing relationships, be it friendships, harmonious coworkers, or intimate connections. Healthy communities have proven to be hotbeds of long life and less disease. Not only does the natural environment impact our wellbeing, but also the camaraderie among people who are striding in the same direction for a greater cause.

A recent analysis of longevity in the Asian population links it, in part, to the disciplined minds that they are cultivating over a lifetime. There is certainly a stress factor that may occur when people overdue this, but on the other hand having a healthy blueprint takes away a lot of the questions and fears that arise from haphazard living. A balanced approach to living requires a combination of consistent progressive patterns, unwavering commitment to fulfillment and a sense of humor to make it light and positive. This triune of successful approaches has been a hallmark in the thousands of people that I have had the pleasure to work with who have achieved healing and recovery.

Sugar, including, dextrose, fructose, sucrose, etc., is one of the biggest culprits in robbing us of longevity and health. We now know that all sugars are thirty times more addictive than cocaine. A Princeton University study compared the brains of heroin addicts, cocaine addicts, and sugar addicts (almost all of us). The sugar lit up the entire brain and advanced the addictive portion more than three dozen times beyond the drugs. Forgive yourself for continuing to cheat and sneak sugar-rich foods under the auspices that they are natural, organic or grow on trees, and move toward a cleaner, healthier palate.

From the Pentagon, they started to add a nerve gas called aspartame as a "so called" sugar substitute and monosodium glutamate, (MSG) as a salt substitute that actually disturbs the nerves and brain. They continue to add thousands of other "additives" and manmade chemicals that promote cancer, organ dysfunction, and even death. With all that said, we are not finished. Cooking doesn't support optimal health, although once you have stabilized the crisis then limited amounts (below 20% by weight) are acceptable. Even the cooking of plant foods and vegetables destroy their health benefits.

Our objective is to abruptly and purposely have you rethink the intimate act of food consumption. We need to come to a place of loving ourselves more than the brainwashing and submission to please others. We need to love ourselves back to health and care about each and every morsel that we put into our bodies. We can thrive, not only survive, on unprocessed, uncooked, raw, organic plant choices. This has been proven clinically here at Hippocrates Health Institute, now in our seventh decade of working with hundreds of thousands of people. Together we can heal ourselves, friends, neighbors, the planet and humanity.

DAIRY FREEDOM

Choices

"The secret of change is to focus all of your energy, not on fighting the old, but on building the new...I know nothing except the fact of my ignorance...Wisdom begins in wonder...Only the extremely ignorant or the extremely intelligent can resist change."

ৎ৯ **Socrates**

Accomplishing self-discovery requires purposeful passion that leads to fulfilling outcomes. The process includes all the food choices that bombard us daily. Science is acutely aware that we need to protect ourselves. We know that good food choices are fundamental for health and prerequisite to shield us from disease.

We are aware that prostate cancer and breast cancer occurrences have reached epidemic proportions with people of all ages. It does not have to be that way! We consistently hear about the benefits of dairy consumption, such as getting calcium and vitamin D, but rarely are we presented with the scientific downfalls of consuming dairy products. The HHI book, *Dairy Deception*, describes how hormones can affect the cells that produce cancer and elucidates on the link between the two to prevent cancer.

Teachers made us consume pints of milk, and fraudulent science told us that this was good for our bones. Even the very glue that was used for art projects was made out of milk; however, children developed asthma and eczema from exposure. What a surprise to learn that the number one dietary cause of cancer is from Casein that is 87 percent of the protein in cow's milk. Elmer's Glue must have known this, because when it was boiled at high temperatures for long periods of time it stuck together and made a perfect adhesive.

When discovering the deception, it was profound to find out that countries worldwide had the same campaigns funded by the dairy industry in cahoots with governments. They poured free milk into our schools, from Russia to the United States, to get us permanently hooked on this non-consumable liquid. It is our responsibility to know what is healthy for us and to make the correct choices for our well-being.

Without having citizens vote on it, the US government became a financial bedmate of this destructive industry profiting from its promotion. It helped get little milk containers into fast food restaurants and school cafeterias across the country. It is easy to see that the milk a calf drinks, which helps them to grow to a thousand pounds, is not the same as a human mother's milk for her offspring.

Many people are allergic to dairy and don't realize the impact that it has on the body. Dairy and grains are the most influential factors causing allergies and impacting the immune system. The best way to understand the difference between the living plant of wheatgrass with that of flour is to go back and restudy basic biology. With germinating grains, the gluten is broken down to amino acids, which avoid allergic reactions.

This is the case with any grain; thus, when it is sprouted and eaten raw there shouldn't be any ill effects arising from gluten concerns. Casein is a protein found in milk, and many are allergic to it. Gluten is a family of proteins found in grains like wheat, rye, spelt and barley. Of the gluten-containing grains, wheat is by far the most commonly consumed. The two main proteins in gluten are glutenin and gliadin. Everyone has a choice, either to continue on the path of disease and death, or to go the bright road of well-being. There are many excuses for not changing, yet there is a lot more data available to support the need to change.

Making good food choices is our constant challenge. As we learn and discover ourselves, we become self-realized, and it will be easier to make better choices. We can build up our immune system by eating living raw foods and master our susceptibility to disease. Each time we reach and accomplish our pinnacle desires, we lay another stone on the path toward our higher purpose. As you ascend to your true self, unfettered forces raise you up, allowing your pure persona to represent your reality. Be brave by being clear and able to accomplish this fearlessly. Accept self-knowledge as a primary goal.

Drs. Anna Maria and Brian share their thoughts about our hopeful and holistic future:

> People, no matter who they are or what their status, will be liberated to craft a happy, healthy, and peaceful life. Balance will once again return to the earth we all inhabit. Futurists predict by mid-twenty-first century, we will all be living more holistically, relying on the abundant and powerful, yet subtle, forces of nature to give us all the energy, well-being, and renewable sustainability required to thrive at maximum levels.
>
> Antiquated ideologies and broken theologies will fall to the wayside as consciousness expands and joy becomes the norm. As amazing as this sounds, it is a reality that you can co-create with those of us who live the dream. You are not alone and we are here for you. Growing into the tens of millions from every corner of the globe, we will surely become billions. Reversing the table of the manipulative powers will be easy since we can use the same

methods they have used, simply by reversing the tide. Economies soon will be based upon renewal, recovery, and harmony.

There have been wise cultures in the past, which have lived in the way that we humans deserve to live. One may argue that it is unrealistic to dream of such balance. Yet, until we dream of such balance and harmony and submit ourselves to its absolute manifestation, it will never occur. Remember, there was a time when people said we could not fly, or communicate within a 20,000-mile distance, or even further back, that the world was flat. Those theories wrong. Why should we assume static dogmas of history should not be challenged? Do you want to join in with committed, optimistic individuals who are willing to go the mile to achieve their ultimate dreams?

Pushing strongly against the tide that resists progress will not work. Rather, establish what the obstacle is, place enormous pressure against it, and then release it so it falls to the wayside. Trying to chip away a little at a time will not result in success, either. Think about everything in your life that you have ever done that was exciting, exhilarating, and fulfilling. We can assure you that it was a result of an abrupt shift in attitude and energy. Reaching the goal was swift, agile, and courageous, not passive, slow, and ineffective.

Engage only in matters that you are committed to transforming. Do not minimize your progress by wasting time on incidental concerns that should be easily dealt with. Focus on the formidable nemeses that block your imagination, weaken your soul, and deplete your energy. Fundamentally, your entire life depends on you creating strong, persevering beliefs that are flexible enough to be altered when your consciousness expands.

Gold medalists, those recovering from catastrophic disease as well as happy, contributory people all share the same mantra: heal thyself by honoring thyself. To honor oneself is to clear the blockages and disorders that limit your spirit. To be in touch with godliness is to be unshackled from your own sadness so you can be elated in your life's passion. Live with a depth of sincerity that allows you to expansively project your desires and at the same time enhance yourself. The ultimate challenge of health and well-being is in your hands. We at HHI are here to continue to support your personal growth and look forward to your success.

NUTRITIONAL ADDITIVES

Experiences

"To enjoy good health, to bring true happiness to all, one must first be disciplined and control one's own mind. If a man can control his mind, he can find the way to enlightenment, and all wisdom and virtue will naturally come to him."

ↄ Buddha

Since we accept the notion that healthy food is necessary to avoid disease, we can evaluate our experiences to expand ourselves. We should not embrace what various industries and institutions tell us since they change their minds. We are the consumers and we have to express our awareness to include what is appropriate. It is our responsibility to choose wisely to avoid pain, suffering and disease.

What if just about everything you thought you knew about supplements and health turned out to be... absolutely wrong? Hippocrates Wellness explores the various myths that have made supplements a "buyer beware" industry. The HHI book, *Supplements Exposed*, strips away layers of deception to reveal the truth about what millions of supplement users each year have taken for granted. For the first time, you will learn how nearly all supplements sold worldwide are synthetics created in pharmaceutical industry labs. As a result, they are potentially toxic.

There are distinct differences between natural (plant-derived) supplements and synthetic (chemically-derived) supplements and how they each impact your health. Nearly all of the medical science studies of nutrients and human health have used synthetics rather than natural nutrients. The HHI *Supplements Exposed* book guides you through the minefield of nutrient choices you face every time you buy vitamins and minerals. It shows you: (1) How to decipher product labels that are otherwise deceptive; (2) How to choose naturally occurring (plant-derived) supplements; (3) Why recommended daily allowances spread confusion, and much more.

Pills we consumed out of a bottle may not be what they were marketed as. Our early examinations shocked us, since it turned out to be a complete and utter fraud. The truth is 90 percent or more of supplements are made in chemical laboratories with either unhealthy materials or manmade chemicals. They have as much to do with nutrients as the sun has to do with the moon.

This multi-billion-dollar industry that still derives most of its raw materials from the pharmaceuticals has convinced the global public that they are malnourished and need their pills to fix the problem they have created. This is true due to the non-foods they are eating. Sadly, rather than producing unprocessed, organic, plant, food-based offerings, they place cheap options in the form of capsules, pills, and powders. This bait and switch method is to get the public to ingest more chemicals and less nutrients which is the opposite of what they need.

Dr. Brian Clement relates the story of Tom Fisher, originally a guest and then a valued staff member for over ten years:

> Two decades ago, a young man attended the Life Transformation Program at Hippocrates Health Institute. He had been diagnosed with stage IV cancer and appeared to be on his last legs after enduring allopathic treatment. I remember so well the sense of desperation and sadness that he projected as I counseled him. He was a collegiate athlete but like most young people lived on sugar, meat and dairy. Exacerbating this, his work became mostly computer-based, spending hours per day in front of a screen. All of the stress came to a head and he began feeling physically weak. When he went to see a physician they told him he was just anemic and that pills would remedy that. Soon after, when Tom was not rebounding, the physician ordered scans and detected a mass. The resulting biopsy determined he had Hodgkin's Lymphoma cancer. Not wanting to believe the diagnosis, he asked for a second opinion which confirmed that he faced a dire prognosis. After adhering to the advised chemotherapy treatments, the physicians sat him down and said at best he had less than a 40 percent chance of surviving for the next five years.
>
> Recognizing the prognosis to be almost hopeless, young Mr. Fisher, began his search for more progressive and holistically traditional ways to heal. Based upon what he had learned attending lectures provided in his hometown of Philadelphia he thought that he had finally found some sort of hope. He chose to come and attend the healing programs that we offer here at Hippocrates. Immediately he began feeling better and within a short time had completely placed his disease in remission. With renewed hope and a desire to now help others, Tom asked me, "If I want to do this work to help others learn what I now know, what are the steps?" I advised him to attend our mastery program and

achieve a degree in nursing. Not only did he accomplish both, but we asked him to join our medical team where he had been an integral part of our counseling and education department for well over ten years.

Tom Fisher, RN is one of tens of thousands of people who share similar recovery stories that I have had the privilege to know and work with over the last half -century. There is such a disparity to what health is and what healthcare should provide. No wonder it seems an enigma when people reverse "incurable" problems with alternative, natural methods.

HHI staff and guests realized that Tom Fisher was very knowledgeable in healthcare and he kept on top of the current research. He exuded the HHI lifestyle and was able to recommend alternative solutions to the health problems many guests found difficult to manage. Tom reduced complex health issues into simple steps that all could follow. We were fortunate to have had Tom's expertise and his willingness to give his precious time to guests and staff.

There is no doubt that when the best fresh food is shipped over days and weeks, many of the nutrients are lost. This is why the utilization of food based, unprocessed supplementation, is essential to maintain health and expedite recovery. It is recommended that the body needs thirty-five supplements daily out of nature's medicine chest. Not only because we lack nutrition, but also because we want more strength, endurance, clarity, and longevity.

Many of the more progressive doctors do not acknowledge the world of difference between a man-made pill and what plants have locked deep in their cells. Even the best of us, who have spent our lives in nutritional science, lack a complete understanding of all the symbiotic elements working together within the botanical kingdom. When respecting this and producing supplements that maintain the integrity rather than arrogantly manipulating it, we receive benefits that we have yet to fully realize. Food is the foremost antidote to disease and premature aging.

As we move forward, the words of Dr. Linus Pauling ring more true. In 1968 he said, "All premature aging and disease is in part due to the lack of vital essential nutrients". Hippocrates Health Institute has surely proven this with the thousands of people who have successfully healed themselves from disease and inevitable short life spans. Knowledge in the area of nutrition is one of the most important and valuable assets that we can acquire. You don't have to become an expert. You just have to become a student of common sense and make a commitment to yourself, your well-being, and the planet at large. Your life and the life of the planet depend on the choices you make.

OCEAN DANGERS

Openness

"Exercise should be regarded as tribute to the heart...To enjoy the glow of good health...A man must fight...Fat is one of the chief enemies of the heart, because it has to be plentifully supplied with blood and thus needlessly increases the pumping load that the heart must sustain."

꿁 **Gene Tunney**

The formula to discover YOU in you is a challenge and can only be accepted if you discard your layers one at a time. Being open means to have the presence of mind to listen, learn, and process new information that might be foreign or incomprehensible to start with. As you then immerse yourself in your unfolding growth, you will discover who you are. This process gives you the tools to achieve a healthy, happy, and fulfilling life. At HHI we provide you the education to learn what is needed for growth. You will expand and become confident, strong, and empathetic. You will find happiness and love.

People the world over are eating more fish than ever before and assuming fish to be a healthful alternative to other meat, as well as an excellent source for omega-3 fatty acids. The HHI book, *Killer Fish*, alerts consumers to how eating aquatic life endangers their health. This book separates myth from fact as it presents powerful evidence of deadly toxins, particularly mercury, plastics, polychlorinated biphenyls (PCBs), and pharmaceuticals. When fish ingest noxious chemicals it travels up the food chain concentrating in tissue of both farmed and wild fish.

When we humans consume toxicity, it alters our health and edges us closer to early demise. We know now of how aquatic life can become contaminated and how fish consumption affects human health. Over fishing is one of the foremost concerns regarding human survival. Genetically modified fish are being released into the wild eventually eradicating natural species. Fish oil has surfaced as a carcinogen and active contributor to cardiovascular disease. For those who depend upon fish as a source of omega-3 fatty acids, a list of safe alternatives, such as algae, chia, flax, or hemp are available.

The far-reaching health consequences suffered by people who eat fish have rocked marine scientists and medical communities around the globe. Modern attempts designed to reverse this plight, such as producing genetically engineered species, have only provided a new set of problems. With the HHI book, *Killer Fish*, the public has a chance to become educated as to the depth of this problem. Hopefully awareness will not only safeguard our health, but be part of the solution.

Most people say they are willing to give up meat, but somehow do not realize that aquatic life is swimming meat, even though we may not see it on farms as we drive by. Additionally, Madison Avenue has elevated fish to health food status; however, it is the exact opposite of what they are suggesting. Even the information on fat content of fish is suspect.

Most fish that people consume today are grown at factory farms. They put thousands of fish in a confined area allowing no room for swimming or ample oxygen for healthy and natural clean exposure. This not only restricts their mobility but reduces the oxygen and nutrient consumption to such a low level that antibiotics are commonly poured into the cages so that the diseased and dying fish will survive until they can be harvested.

The so-called foods fed to them is not natural for these creatures. They often grind up fish mixed with grains, then add this to "feed" that is commonly genetically modified. Salmon is the most notable fish since they have you believing that Eskimos are catching them in midair as they are jumping out of pristine rivers and wild, untouched waters. This is simply not the case.

Recent studies show that the vast majority of these creatures are grown in Asia in untenable polluted cesspools. Myths prevail at such high level around the consumption of aquatic life. This is not surprising since the majority of health professionals propagate misinformation on this subject.

The omega-3 oils that the fish consume come from algae. Intelligent consumers ingest the algae directly and not from the disease-causing middle man. Lobsters are a popular delicacy; however, certain religious sects refrain from their consumption, since lobsters are scavengers. To top it all off, we smother it in butter before we devour it.

Oceanographic scientists and marine biologists tell us that soon we will not have to worry about aquatic life, since by mid-century we will have fished out the major schools from the ocean. Like other meat substitutes, today there is an emerging fish substitute industry that is slowly offering healthy choices to avoid the cancer causing elements that are in these creatures.

We should recognize that most of the ideas that we have on what is good for us come from the very industry that produces the product. Lobbyists with governments worldwide, guide politicians to permit unthinkable activities in the production of fish.

We have known, for more than six decades that within twenty to thirty minutes of removing aquatic life from their natural environment, their flesh and oils become rancid, contributing to cardio and cancer concerns. Even the "taste" of fish comes more from the bacteria of the decomposing animal than the meat itself.

For most of us, life has become a circular vacuum where we jump in becoming fully engaged in the nothingness of everything. As time passes, this abnormal state becomes comfortable for most, and we institutionalize that abnormality. This base standard literally becomes social norm and completely accepted. How is it that with all of the access we have to knowledge, we have chosen the lowest common denominator and even created a façade that it is truth? There is only one explanation for this phenomenon and that is the almost universal lack of core values that people possess today.

Drs. Brian and Anna Maria emphasize the importance of taking responsibility of your own restorative potential:

> Somehow our memory of our inherent healing power has diminished to a negligible point. Our great grandparents innately knew how to take care of themselves. Their families instinctually chose foods and "herbal medicine" from their local environment. We are now so paralyzed emotionally that we do not trust ourselves in making the pinnacle decisions that relate to our very survival. Layer after layer of deceptive systems and propaganda have us believing that we have to go to others to ask how we should live, heal, and thrive.

You are in total control and it is a waste of energy and time to divert your attention from that very fact. Yes, at times you may need assistance, guidance, and support, but nobody, including those you love, can make you well. This has been Hippocrates Health Institute's contribution to the present and future of health care. Once you begin supporting the body and its brilliant immune system, it appears as though magic occurs. This is biochemistry at its best. Although studies on this fact have not been funded by major industry, it was created by the evolutionary process that the very universe sparked.

There is no doubt that the cusp of a new reality awaits you when you have knowledge, tools, and inner power to prevent and reverse disorder. Perplexing thoughts rain down on you when you ask, "How You are in total control and it is a waste of energy and time to divert your attention from that very fact. Yes, at times you may need assistance, guidance, and support, but nobody, including those you love, can make you well. This has been Hippocrates Health Institute's contribution to the present and future of health care. Once you begin supporting the body and its brilliant immune system, it appears as though magic occurs. This is biochemistry at its best. Although studies on this fact have not been funded by major industry, it was created by the evolutionary process that the very universe sparked.

There is no doubt that the cusp of a new reality awaits you when you have knowledge, tools, and inner power to prevent and reverse disorder. Perplexing thoughts rain down on you when you ask, "How do I know what to do?" Shut off the mind and redirect the question to your heart. It will certainly respond correctly if you give it enough time. Not knowing any better is the reason for making bad decisions, eating poorly, taking stimulants, or laying around. When you are pursuing harmful lifestyle choices, in your heart and soul you know better. There is no dilemma or confusion on this matter; it is only your willingness and love for yourself that is required to move forward.

In the future, we will look back at this historic time with empathy for the suffering masses who have been hijacked as guinea pigs, piggy banks and victims to the greed of corporations in the medical field. All the so-called oddballs who are screaming at the top of the mountains about personal responsibility for individual health, will emerge as pioneering figures in humanity's advancement. This unstoppable movement will finally expose the corrupt pursuits of the so-called healthcare system.

Wanting to belong, without a contribution to offer, entices us to accept and embrace modern dogma that has little or nothing to do with important pillars of certainty. Although it is essential for all of us to share, commune, and relate, we never should arrive at the party without a gift. What is your contribution? Have you ever thought about your greatest attribute? If this question perplexes you, the roadmap to find your self-realized gift is that which you love the most. Knowing yourself and all your gifts and talents is a process of discovery and adventure.

Ironically, the most passionate thing you want to pursue is your contribution. This endowment is what you should happily share. Consider this, it is almost as if you are a channel between the universe and all other life. You are the pristine cascade that dispenses pure joy and elation to others who rally along with you in sincerity. Your importance is unquestionable; you came to this world to leave behind something of value, and there never should be a question as to whether you can fulfill this inherent obligation.

HEALTHY ALTERNATIVES

Realization

"Worthless people love to eat and drink; people of worth eat and drink only to live...Only one thing I know, that is I know nothing... Nothing is to be preferred before justice...The best seasoning for food is hunger; for drink, thirst."

ـْۄ **Socrates**

Once you are open to your purpose in life and value the importance of appropriate food selection you will become healthy. Your ability to choose wisely will expand. You will confidently continue to make prudent choices in all your endeavors. It is time to accept change, and the new YOU.

Choosing to live a healthy life will occur after you realize there are no other choices than to accept the inevitable. You suddenly realize that you choose Life and not the death march of eating foods that cause disease. The choices are there and now you have the wisdom to make the good decisions for yourself to extend life. Our culture is unaware of the plight of the poultry system. Most farms and institutions use inhumane and disease producing environments to house birds.

The HHI book, *Poison Poultry*, expounds on how eating poultry and their eggs undermines your health. This book cites incredible research that will allow you, your family and friends to make more informed food choices. This research clears up the myths that you and others have been taught since early childhood, and will reframe your perspective on what you select to eat. This discovery and many other alarming facts will transform the way you think.

An environmental biologist recently stated that if all slaughtered creatures were able to roam over the earth, we'd have to remove all buildings and have seven earths for the amount of dead animals sold as organic meat. At least three nights a week most people have eaten chicken or turkey for their main meal, as well as eggs for breakfast. Thank goodness they did not like the taste of duck or quail, as these were somewhat of a "delicacy."

We have warped and morphed the bodies of turkeys so much that they can no longer procreate. Even the so-called free-range variety requires artificial insemination. In the same factory farms, they take particular buildings and put a sign "organic" on them. The poultry business self-regulates, and by opening the windows for thirty minutes a day, they can legally call the poultry "free-range" and organic. The free-range chickens are so packed into one space that they smother and defecate on each other and many die in this buried alive, toxic state. There are many horror stories of how poultry is handled.

As we investigate different farms, there are many different poultry management systems. You may find cage-less eggs where it has been estimated 15 percent higher death since the animals are now walking on top of one another in an over crowed environment. The ones on the bottom often die of urine ammonia poisoning. Chickens and turkeys have far more saturated fat than steak, which we have been told to avoid due to its disease-causing properties.

Have you or someone you know and love been diagnosed with either breast or colon cancer? With alarming rates of increase in these cancers, coupled with the scientific proof of the bodily harm from eating poultry and eggs, there should be little surprise. Concerning the relationship of egg consumption to breast cancer risk, thirteen separate scientific studies were analyzed in 2014. According to the research analysts, these "results" showed that egg consumption was associated with increased breast cancer risks for those who consume five eggs or more per week.

Ethical scientists are now catching up with the knowledge of the disease producing problems with poultry and egg consumption. Specifically, this knowledge is associated with increased breast cancer risk among consumers. The post-menopausal population and those who consumed two to five eggs per week are also susceptible.

Chicken and eggs have been positioned by their industries as "healthful options" for many years. Are they feeding us lies? The HHI book *Poison Poultry* has delved into deeply rooted misconceptions and discusses what it really affects. What is evident is that we were never meant to eat birds and possibly the vengeance that they have on us now is the ever blossoming disorders that are common to our species.

Dr. Anna Maria relates the importance of a conscious lifestyle:

With consciousness rising and business booming, a subtle yet powerful conflict began in people's lives. High-speed living became faster and faster and technology fueled our need to move even quicker on an almost ongoing basis. Quick and convenient became our mantra for breakfast, lunch, and dinner. Working hours have not stopped increasing, affording us less time for recreation and exercise. Ironically, with all the fitness opportunities we have today, in developed countries less than 5 percent of the population exercise adequately.

Obesity has become commonplace and now the World Health Organization and others tell us that four out of five people in our western world are overweight or obese. To top this all off, companies have become so greedy that they laced common "foods" with addictive sugars and synthetic chemicals that mimic opiates. Globally, health care systems are at the economic breaking point since lethargic junk food lifestyles are the cause and the core of most disease and premature aging.

In 1956, the sun rose in Boston, Massachusetts, when Hippocrates Health Institute, the world's first Lifestyle Modification

Center, launched the now-emerging field of Lifestyle Medicine. Founder Ann Wigmore correctly and innately knew that what was missing in all healthcare was people's personal participation. We have forgotten how to live naturally and healthily as our grand and great grandmothers had done. Synthetics, chemicals and electronics replaced organic and natural living that humans had thrived in throughout history.

Coming out of the rabbit hole requires committed consciousness that propels infinite awareness and powerful conviction. As you emerge from the cyclical system of silliness, you will first feel alone and then eventually find others who live painlessly with happiness. All struggles come from the disconnection we have within ourselves. There is never a problem that cannot be resolved by you. As unpleasant as it may be to go through the process and challenge of change, you ultimately broaden your capacity and strengthen your values by doing so. Clarity, focus, and feverish enthusiasm are hallmarks that all true participants share. Life never brings you sadness; it is how you process what you are experiencing that determines the outcome. The depth of self-realization is what brings about unbridled energy to conquer these dilemmas.

Living in each and every one of our hearts is a fierce dragon of love. This enormous creature is your best friend and needs to be fed, rested, and exercised. All too often, it feels abandoned and left impotent to help you navigate a peaceful and fruitful life. Engage this cohort by embracing the power within and utilizing it to forge a new path to your destiny. Goals are for you to imagine and, more importantly, for you to achieve.

The year 1956 manifested Ann Wigmore's vision in the form of the Hippocrates Health Institute. We have continued to nurture her dream and mission statement, "Help people help themselves," which organically produced innumerous healings. As our current team often states, "We help people love the disease right out of themselves."

For so many who are so loved, it is still often not enough to be able to accept themselves. When people do not have support, needless to say, it is even more difficult to find true inner acceptance.

Now in our seventh decade, we can clearly state that each person has the ability to transform their life. This is not a miraculous process, but rather a simple proposition. Becoming YOU is becoming whole. When becoming whole, all is there to empower your healing. Although food is central, and productive movement is required, it is self-realization and self-respect that finally accomplishes the life you deserve to live. Recognizing your current reality and imagining your optimum state are your tickets to health, happiness, and healing.

HUMAN HEALTH

Additional Stories

The mid-twentieth century was the tipping point for social change that sparked the rise of awareness. The burgeoning economies in the west made available education that was paralleled with the beginnings of what has blossomed into the information age. No longer were we colloquially encapsulated in a small world of conformity. For the first time in human history people were asking questions and jumping off the assembly line mentality that had maintained order in generations past.

At this very moment there was a shift in power from people to corporations. Many of these nefarious organizations recognized that television was a vehicle to disseminate their products and philosophies. Madison Avenue cohorts worked with PhD psychologists in planning ways to shift attitudes, purchasing trends, and even culture. One of the first examples was their marketing to the youngest among us on children's programming. Everything from sugar-laden breakfast cereals to hosts telling children to take money out of their mother's pocketbooks and mail it to them, which unfortunately proved successful.

They framed the teen years by harvesting the minds and hearts of future adults and making it hip to hang out in fast food "locals." This was a new way to manage the minds of the population through mass advertising and news media efforts. All of this began a generation before and was spearheaded by the tobacco industry that made it sexy to smoke. They even used more incriminating methods such as saying most doctors smoke a particular brand, showing the rat pack of society smoking at the Oscars, and positioning the "Marlboro Man" as the quintessential male, etc.

One by one, Wigmore and her team reintroduced the guests who attended the Institute to simple, common-sense approaches to life. Hundreds of thousands of people have partaken in the transformative programs that this pioneering organization has consistently offered during the last several decades. Organically, through the eyes of the clinical team, trends emerged that concretely developed understanding of the essential elements necessary to prevent and reverse disease and premature aging. Scientists worldwide from endless universities and organizations began producing research results that not only supported but also confirmed the work that Hippocrates Wellness is engaged in.

Dr. Brian shares his views on friend and colleague, Andy Roman, RN, who has been in the HHI family from the early Florida years:

Three decades ago we brought Andy Roman LM, LMHC, RN in as our psychotherapist. His multifaceted and comprehensive background in healthcare afforded him unique tools in seeing how the human mind functions. Realizing, as he states, "the body follows what's in the heart and mind," he counsels people who are often in the grips of serious illness about the importance of affirmative thought. During one of Roman's signature therapy Healing Circles, a Vietnam War veteran confessed his innermost belief. He stated, "I don't deserve to get well for all of the horrible things I did when at war." One of the other participants in this group session, a Vietnamese woman, blared out "We forgive you" and stood to hug him.

What an extraordinary moment for both of these individuals, who harbored their own unique scars from the same experience. There was not a dry eye in the house for this intimate healing circle. There began his process to fully recover from a chronic autoimmune disorder. Sometimes it's just a simple gesture of forgiveness or listening that erases the self-imposed pain of guilt that people harbor sometimes for a lifetime.

On a daily basis, we watch Roman wrestle the demons out of people that perceive themselves as broken victims. As Andy states, "The only wisdom is body wisdom." Shrink the mind, body gap with DEEP FEELING THERAPY. It is our shallow, callous concepts that govern most of our bad decisions. The only way to resolve these issues is to dive deep into our authentic mindset. That is where the destruction occurs and self-abuse is born. Until revealing this demon of doubt, it is impossible to release patterns of self-destruction.

You must tell it like it is. Do not under or overstate. At times you must practice this process of purging so that you can replace disorder with order, and pain with purpose. Confess to yourself by bearing your own soul. Unearthing all flaws and shortcomings. This permits a realistic evaluation of your own destructive patterns. Roman's psychotherapy is more about percepive imagination that ultimately initiates change. When you are locked into a merry-go-round of confusion and thought patterns, it is nearly impossible to raise yourself to the highest level of function. It is there, well beyond the suffocation of your own perceived limitations, that creation of a viable existence occurs.

The goal of deep feeling therapy is to reach the body's cells with new information, not just reach the person's intellect with insight. Every cell has to be reprogrammed with new positive data that clears the decks for a revived and brilliant future. The Greek word for healing, "Holos," (meaning wholeness) calls you to take daily responsibility for your overall health. All healing is to complete you so that, like a wheel, you can roll proactively in a progressive direction that will enrich and enhance your every move. Andy's therapy methods have proven to be very effective.

There are many different modalities of psychotherapy. You may consider working with a "new school" psychotherapist that is not shackled with the historic and pragmatic impositions of conventional psychology. Changing your view of reality actually changes reality. Every step that you make needs to have a foundation of self-realization. Undoubtedly, each of us exists to increase and further advance our submission to the omni-present ether that surrounds us.

Your biology depends upon your mentality and it is that very mentality that either aids or erodes your health. Over time, the HHI staff has had the honor to work with people who have created spontaneous remission from disease. Although unexplainable in allopathic realms, it is clear as to how this works. Placebo is something every healthcare professional eventually acknowledges. A person/patient's belief in their treatment, protocol, or pursuit enables them to diminish and even eradicate formidable disorders. This accepted phenomena has been the number one scientifically unexplained event studied over the last century.

Somehow mainstream practitioners and their academic partners have intentionally ignored the power of thought. Granted, thought in and of itself, is not curative, but when accompanied by affirmative lifestyle and/or treatment actions, positive results arise. A study recently published concerned seven patients with pancreatitis. Each was prepared for surgery yet only three actually received the procedure. Ironically three of the four remaining who believed they had undergone the treatment but only received the placebo effect, fully recovered from their ailment without having received any medical intervention.

In the fifth century BC on the Greek Island of Kos, Hippocrates, the father of western medicine, conducted talk therapy with each of his patients before he ever suggested physical means of treatment. He was searching the souls of the afflicted to mine the cause of their affliction. Once he sensed what was really bothering them, he instinctually tailored a plan of action that could alleviate their problem.

Ironically, the modern healthcare system has dehumanized the process. Rush to action has replaced sensitivity to circumstance. For this reason, medical mistakes have risen as the third major killer in the developed world. Everyone is looking for the magic pill rather than creating the magic within themselves and their lives.

Brian relates his initial encounter with Dr. Jan Hranicky Ph.D., M.D., the founder and president of The American Health Institute, Inc.:

Twenty years ago I began working with Dr. Jan Hranicky who now leads Hippocrates Comprehensive Cancer and Chronic Immune Disorder Program. She is not only a world-renowned psycho-neuro-immunologist, she was partnered with well-known visionary, Dr. Carl Simonton. Dr. Jan worked at his side for a quarter of a century. She has studied to become a medical doctor and has an extensive background in science and in all areas of advanced progressive healthcare. She, like me, practices quantum medicine and has comprehensive experience in the fields of energy medicine.

Dr. Jan Hranicky guides the premier cancer program that is offered at Hippocrates Wellness. She has given me an opportunity to observe her brilliant strategies when deposing an individual so that they reveal their tendency toward traits of self-sabotage. Combining energy medicine with the perpetual frequency of talk therapy can rapidly release the restrictive emotions that the afflicted person possesses. There is not one case ever that does not require an emotional purge resulting in a physical shift.

Cancer and autoimmune disease, as Dr. Hranicky states, can be dealt with by "activating your own healing mechanisms for getting well and staying well." Her contagious positivity is certainly part of the antidote that her patients experience during their transformation and healing. Dr. Jan is noted for her research connecting stress and emotions that can feed cancer. She developed an innovative model incorporating her training in Bioenergetic Regeneration Medicine, along with her exciting work with the Bioenergy Field Foundation.

As appealing as it is to pigeon hole particular procedures that will so-call "cure a disease," it is not as simple as that. Multi-faceted dimensions in human beings require multifaceted methodologies, treatments and lifestyle changes to reach true success. All too often we are lulled into believing that when we cut out a tumor we are cured without asking where it came from to begin with. Is it possible that it may grow back? Are the billions of cells that physically created it simply gone? After symptoms wane from medicating ourselves, is a virus totally gone or just dormant?

Many people experience a cold sore that lies dormant and can break out on the lip from stress. These little bugs are waiting for immunity to plummet so they can reemerge as your lifelong nemeses. The Pasteurian Idea that all disease is born out of invisible microbes is not the full story that Louis Pasteur himself acknowledged.

Two thirds of our bodies harbor bacteria; therefore, when hygiene and health are maintained, most that's left are positive probiotics. When we indulge in haphazard, modern living, we slowly destroy these health-building microbes and replace them with bad bacteria. This is why illness is commonplace even among the youngest. Infants often begin their lives being injected with vaccines and flushed with antibiotics. Before taking a first step or saying their initial word, their little immune systems are compromised. External environments and the very clothes adorning their small bodies begin polluting their systems with chemicals, fire retardants, plastics, and other poisons.

Cancer is one of the most formidable disorders suffered by babies. Two generations ago, this would have been such an oddity that researchers globally would be interested in how it may have occurred. Life expectancy is plummeting and in the last decade has dropped by several years. Additionally new disorders are presenting themselves, such as Lyme's, chronic fatigue, or the explosion in diabetes, etc.

There is a clear and definitive answer to all of this frightening news. Hippocrates Wellness has led hundreds of thousands toward regaining their balance by employing proper nutrition, enhanced positive thought, and increased physical activity, supplemented by non-invasive therapies in the quest to reverse disease and premature aging. Documented case after documented case has been the result of decades of work that stands as a model for future healthcare. Billions of dollars are being spent to look for the short cut when the answer is standing in front of us.

Dorothy Lake, a New York City executive, endured extreme mental, emotional and physical hardships. She lost three important relationships, her mother, father and husband. She relates her story:

On October 10, 2001 we were notified that Bill's remains had been found exactly where I knew he would be. In the stairwell, on the 56th floor of the north tower. The stairwell where, rest assured, he was humping 80 pounds of gear escorting people out to safety. At this point, I lost my father to cancer and I had just managed the care of my mother (living with us full time now) with stage IV lung cancer which had metastasized to her colon. Also, I had a grieving and post traumatic six-year-old little boy in my care. I had to pull my big girl boots up and carry the team on my back and steer this ship forward. I remembered being around that table every day baking and decorating cupcakes for my son for his birthday with the realization that no matter what happens or what was happening, I needed to be fully present in the moment and available and joyous. What was important for the people that were in my life now was that they came first.

This is how I live my life each day. I remind myself to "look at my feet" and "face forward" to get myself back to the present moment and get my mind out of the past. My mother lost her battle with cancer and passed away in 2004. It was then that I felt a shift in my overall well-being and health. I had just buried three of the most important people in my life and only had two people of significant left in this realm, my son and my sister. In the aftermath of 9/11, teams from the NYU Hospital Child Study Center along with Harvard University's Trauma Study Center came to work with our families after the devastation. My son drew a picture called "three beds in the dirt" to represent his beloved father, grandmother and grandfather, all dying before he turned nine years old.

It is only as an individual that people enjoy similar interests and experiences. For example, many people experience happiness with their pets or with their children and grandchildren.

Once you know you are happy, like the beginning of a wonderful marriage, partnership or alliance, you have to maintain this connection and level of happiness. Yes, it goes up and down like all things do, and fluctuates, but you have to be clear on what is present. Things may fall apart, however, the way to assess real and true happiness is to recognize when it is missing.

Our voyage is just beginning, as we still have a lot to do with regard to abuse and sex trafficking. We acknowledge that we are starting to make inroads in many of the world's arenas; however, there is still much that future generations will have to address to allow the female population to hold their power. Currently progress is being made; however, male domination is still in control and females still have to work even harder to get a shift in the paradigm.

We have to reeducate the public on the essential importance of being proactive in their own lives. Corporations mislead since they care less about us and more about their profits. How have we fallen to such a low level that keeping people just sick enough to be on medication, but not dead, is the norm for the majority? It is not surprising that we find ourselves some of the sickest inhabitants who have ever resided on planet earth. As unthinkable as it is, millions of children's brains are being silenced by psychiatric medicines while the most likely causes of their problems are their hazardous diets and excessive use of electromagnetic devices. Changing daily habits may not be easy but it would resolve the overwhelming majority of the health-destroying maladies that we all face.

Brian relates his respect and esteem for his colleague Antony Chatham who has degrees in many therapy and philosophical fields:

In the 1990s, we brought Antony Chatham, Master's in Philosophy, Master's in Theology, MSW, and LCSW to the Institute as a psychotherapist. Formerly a priest with pastoral training, he dynamically expanded his repertoire by achieving master's degrees in advanced therapeutic techniques. He often tells the people he counsels that the first doctors stated, "It is more important to know what sort of person has a disease than to know what sort of disease a person has." He accessed traditional Chinese medicine and Ayurvedic techniques. Thousands of years ago these techniques pointed out that: spleen and stomach problems relate to worry, liver and gallbladder to anger and frustration, lungs and large intestine to sadness and suppressed grief, kidney and bladder to fear and shock, and heart and small intestine relate to joy or lack thereof.

So many people today suffer post-traumatic stress, eating disorders, phobias, sexual abuse, panic attacks, disturbing memories, performance anxiety, physical abuse, grief, anxiety disorders, addictions, and pain. When these core concerns are unresolved, they can devour our mind's energy, and body's strength. There are emotional and mental techniques that we have observed Chatham employ on our program guests, and so often they have stated that the burden has been lifted and they can viably measure physical and emotional change.

Studies have shown that when you register a loud sound, your body literally shuts down and you stop breathing. This stressful event portrays the effects that trauma has on your health. We all possess different levels of shutting down. In the worst cases, people are literally dysfunctional and unable to live life at even minimal levels.

Health

In the Hippocrates program, Antony uses many different treatment modalities of which Guided Imagery, Eye Movement Desensitization and Reprocessing (E.M.D.R.), Clinical Hypnosis, and Neuro-Linguistic Programming (NLP), are most commonly employed. Antony uses EMDR, which is a form of psychotherapy that was developed to resolve symptoms resulting from disturbing and unresolved life experiences. He uses a structured approach to address past, present, and future aspects of disturbing memories.

Antony Chatham views some level of stress in life as inevitable; it is part of living. There's bad stress and good stress. Good stress is when someone falls in love, or gets a promotion in their job. Bad stress or "distress" affects our physical and mental health and prevents us from experiencing true happiness in life. Bad stress can overwhelm us with negative emotions like anger, fear, anxiety, sadness, and guilt. Stress can cause the immune system to be on hold. The physical conditions attributed to stress usually include heart diseases, cancers, autoimmune diseases, obesity, insomnia, and chronic pain.

Mahatma Gandhi, stated so well "The weak can never forgive" and "Forgiveness is the attribute of the strong." Ironically, when one is not well, it is hard to conjure up enough positive energy to forgive the very issues that are blocking healing, and even more so when people are at their lowest level. However, it is necessary to provoke our inner strength to abolish the malaise of self-destruction.

We have developed a team of highly motivated professionals who have passionately employed years of specialized work in the quest of helping people resolve their issues. There is often one word or one act that ushers someone down the path to self-healing. Although it appears that the food, talk therapy, medicine or physical adjustments are the reasons for the remission of ANT (Automatic Negative Thoughts) disorder, it is actually the self-acceptance by the recipient that liberates and heals.

For example, you may have the finest orchestra on earth but if the entire violin section is absent, it will not raise the performance to the anticipated glorious level. Your physical and emotional healing requires all musicians to be seated so that the conductor (you) can smoothly execute the desired symphony. We can learn from the knowledge of current gifted individuals as well as those from ancient times.

Here is Anna Maria's "virtual interview" with Hippocrates (c. 460 BCE – c. 370 BCE):

A few years ago, we were the keynote speakers at a two-day conference in Athens, Greece. Some of our medical colleagues, who also presented, were scholars on the father of medicine. So it provoked me to further delve into the work of this enormous figure.

He was the son of Heraclides and Praitela. He was a pupil of his father, who instructed him in physics and all the liberal arts as well as life's miracles. His parents desired him to leave his town and he practiced in all parts of Greece.

A few years ago, we were the keynote speakers at a two-day conference in Athens, Greece. Some of our medical colleagues, who also presented, were scholars on the father of medicine. So it provoked me to further delve into the work of this enormous figure.

He was the son of Heraclides and Praitela. He was a pupil of his father, who instructed him in physics and all the liberal arts as well as life's miracles. His parents desired that he leave his town. He practiced in all parts of Greece. He was a great observer with lots of case studies. The plague was raging in Athens, which began in Ethiopia, then Egypt and Libya, where the Persian governor asked for Hippocrates' assistance to help with their army. This brought great fame.

After his death, his sons, or those who succeeded him, found papers, and published Hippocrates' work. In the words below, I will conduct a virtual interview with him. Hopefully, I will do him justice and give all of you insight into why he is called the father of western medicine.

Anna Maria: Where did you live and pioneer your form of medicine?

Hippocrates: I was born on Kos island between Greece and Turkey in 460 B.C. As a boy, I was influenced by the great philosophers that were fellow citizens of Greece.

Anna Maria: Who was the most influential teacher?

Hippocrates: It began with my father who was compassionate, caring and thought of as a healer. Although I spent much of my time in Western Asia Minor, not the Greek mainland. Plato rang true in my heart and mind. Socrates philosophically resonated with my soul.

Anna Maria: When working with a person who is sick, what are the three most important area that you pursue?

Hippocrates: After the person accepts themselves fully, I hold that the diet and food which people consume and drink should be similar to the ox, the horse, and all other animals. We must eat of the earth, such as fruits, weeds and grass, for such things we grow, live free of disease, and require no other substance.

Anna Maria: How does the mind and the diet create disease?

Hippocrates: We suffered much and severely from a strong and brutish diet, swallowing things which are poison. We create through unhealthy fare strong pains, diseases and early deaths. You must possess a clear mind to make good choices, including that which we eat.

Anna Maria: You speak about seasons and their importance in life.

Hippocrates: Consider the season of the year, then the winds, the hot and the cold. The sunrise, settings of the stars. manifest in troublesome symptoms. When the body is purging itself of microbes and acute inflammation, you may observe fever accompanied by the tongue becoming black. The eyes are hollow, with heart burn, headache and mouth taste bitter. They feel weak, with poor digestion and elimination. Additionally, there may be bowel discomfort with a yellow watery discharge. Intense thirst, insomnia, and sometimes wandering of the mind, cold extremities and overall weakness. For this, I suggest to restrict consumption of salty and acidic foods or drink, indulge in flaxseed water (2 tablespoons flaxseed per one quart of water) and diluted vinegar. Encourage cleansing of the bowel with water enema to help evacuation, including laxatives. Raise body temperatures to a critical sweat (sauna) and drink until urine is clear, sleep in a dark room, keeping your feet, ears and neck warm. Bathing is essential, when in good health and for pneumonia since it soothes the pain in chest and back, promotes expectoration; improves the respiration, removes heaviness of the head and moistens the nose.

Anna Maria: Which common foods cause problems?

Hippocrates: Bread creates swelling of the belly due to its indigestible properties. Flesh of creatures is not desirable and the milk they secrete causes foul intestines. The strength of the patient is to be taken into consideration, additionally, their constitution. Some were eating whatever came their way, cheese, honey, wine, and some took care.

Anna Maria: How do you help those with skeletal and tissue concerns:

Hippocrates: My precise instruction for the anatomy and how to treat it after traumas has to do with readjustment. For example, thin, slender people have more problems with shoulder dislocation, i.e., the head of the humerus is felt in the armpits. When the patient cannot raise their arm. I strongly place my fist in the armpit and abruptly raise it. At times, we slowly raise the body temperature, placing hands on the affected area and determining which direction to pull or push.

Anna Maria: Does digestion play a role?

Hippocrates: When bodies are not properly cleansed, the more you nourish, the more you injure. Debris prevents food from causing strength. Evacuations should be judged by how strong they are. When bowels are loaded with feces, an enema (clyster) should be administered. The symptoms of dysentery are loose dark stools and dark urine with no appetite. The greatest and most dangerous diseases that are fatal are consumption, no appetite, or no thirst.

Anna Maria: Why did you feel it necessary to create a new form of medicine?

Hippocrates: Medicine would not have been invented at first – but due to how we eat and drink, all other "animals" eat what they are supposed to, fruits, weeds and grass, except man. The way we process – grilling, toasting, roasting – changing from natural to weakened state. Nature would not do this, so the medicine was given for the health of man for his nourishment and safety as a substitute for that kind of diet by which pains, diseases, and deaths were occasional. Many are barbarian and refuse to take heed.

Anna Maria: Comprehensively, name all of the tools you use as a physician.

Hippocrates: Positive thoughts, pure diet, anatomical adjustment, fasting, and cleansing. The stars and seasons, the body's river and its pressure points, hydro and hyperthermia. Ocean waves, rivers, streams, and hot springs act as stimulators and purge disease.

This "virtual interview" allowed Anna Maria to deeply connect with Hippocrates' work which revealed his infinite genius. Astonishingly, with laser like extrasensory perception, he borrowed from traditional methods and foresaw the need to pioneer new areas of exploration. To call his approach holistic would be a disservice to his universal approach. Impatiently, he challenged methods and procedures practiced by physicians that were his contemporaries.

He recognized, nearly 2500 years ago, what the greater public is now understanding about the practice of medicine. Limitations within standard practice destroy the inspiration to conquer ills of any magnitude. From his foundational empathetic and compassionate work his legacy can be summed up in one word, "Limitless."

Over time, we hope that you will learn to utilize the practices, methods, and teachings that we have been unifying since the 1950s.

Section II

HAPPINESS

SELF-REALIZED INTEGRITY

INSPIRATION   CALM

""A happy life must be to a great extent a quiet life, for it is only
in an atmosphere of quiet that true joy dare live...The good life is
one inspired by love and guided by knowledge...To conquer fear is
the beginning of wisdom...Critical thinking is required for making up
one's own mind...All behavior springs from desire..."

                                              ⌐ Bertrand Russell

*H*appiness thrives in self-realized individuals. Knowing our
purpose is a result of honest self-evaluation. Acquiring happiness in
one's life is a pursuit that we, in our world, relish and are searching for
every day. We know that when we are self-actualized, we are open to

experience joy. Many say it is only internal happiness we can grasp; however, being able to cope with external mishaps can affect our state of calm. When we are secure, peaceful, and joyous we are prepared to experience bliss. We achieve the best of ourselves with the help of nature and our five senses.

People have cited many achievements that contribute to happiness such as, money, work, family, etc.; however, we can only be fulfilled for a moment since we live in the present. The purpose of meditation or prayer is to keep us focused while fostering a calm mind free of fear and worry. Acceptance of self and others is necessary for happiness and ultimate bliss. Caring for others renders less stress and a joyous life. We need to learn to nourish our thoughts.

We are able to experience bliss, if we are free to be ourself. When discovering our gifts we will open. We need to explore and love everything around us, including nature. Bliss is the highest form of happiness and is strengthened with spirituality. The spiritual self is aware of nature and the beauty that abounds. If we are immersed in material wealth or greed, we harbor a superficial life in a shallow bubble with no purpose. Self-awareness is paramount. Only YOU, within you, can make yourself truly happy.

Happiness with health and joy breeds good social interactions, as well as fulfillment, and feelings of belonging. There are several HHI books that depict the theme of happiness. This theme has many facets as demonstrated in the behaviors listed below:

1. ACKNOWLEDGMENT — producing a state of well-being without trauma or worry. Living a peaceful and calm life involves knowing we cannot change other people; however, self-knowledge gives us strength to accept what is and to make correct choices for physical and mental health. We only can change our attitude and perspective.

The HHI book associated with this theme is *Living Foods for*

Optimum Health, since choosing healthy foods to reach our potential (physically, emotionally, and mentally) is one of our main goals. We can only achieve this through awareness and allowing ourselves to select optimal foods that nourish and help us achieve our potential or higher spiritual self.

2. PRESENCE — allowing ourselves to understand who we are and to be open to energy which attracts what we need for our higher selves. When we embrace arts or sports, our body can be in the "zone" and time does not exist. We are only present and our best if free of self-sabotage.

The HHI book associated with this theme is *LifeForce*, since ridding the body of poisons helps us transform our lifestyle from toxic to renewed energy. We need to strengthen our natural defenses to maintain immunity free from illness. Only then can we reach the initial force that has maximum power to be our best, free of disease, depression, and anxiety.

3. CREATIVITY — reaching our higher level of self is the road to happiness where we allow only good energy to flow by blocking any adversity to achieve our foremost goals. Our intelligence is at its pinnacle when we are creative and imaginative. Everyone can achieve their top level through discipline, acknowledgment, faith, and honesty.

The HHI book associated with this theme is *Longevity*, since living a long life implies being content and making enhanced choices. This process involves living in a state of creativity or a lifestyle conducive to being happy and doing things that you enjoy. People that we welcome can participate in this sharing process, as well as loved ones.

4. BELONGING — being in a family of relatives or friends affords us the lifestyle to participate in activities to feel connected. We feel we belong when we are accepted for who we are and not constantly criticized or bullied. Ironically, it is the bullies who need more love and support to overcome their negativity.

The HHI book associated with this theme is *Healthful Cuisine*, since our need to share our gifts allows us to prepare healthy meals for friends and relatives. Family gatherings are where we express our personal desires for happiness. Food is the universal gift we share with each other to depict belongingness and love.

5. SPIRITUALITY — living a life within our higher mental self can help guide us to rise above the lower self to reaching the true self. We will survive our negative feelings if we can manage to keep our sense of pure energy or spirit alive living within us. Life is mundane without a higher sense of purpose keeping us motivated and happy.

The HHI book associated with this theme is *Emo-Spirit*, since we can only be spiritual once we master our turbulent negative emotional selves. Our spiritual level is reflected in a calm emotional state. When we are so present that our breath is one with our atmosphere, we then begin to reflect our spirituality. Time doesn't exist if we are one with nature.

6. ADAPTABILITY – having a personality that can change to suit uncertain events as we transform and evolve. As we age, we go through difficult passages. Our mental health depends on adapting to our surroundings. Our external environment fosters affirmative action. We need to strengthen our internal voice via coping skills for new disturbances.

The HHI book associated with this theme is *Man-Opause*, since our male companions and friends are challenged via physical, emotional, and mental changes occurring within their realm. Only when we are aware of changes can we prepare ourselves for new situations. As we grow through many decades (passages), we potentially learn to incorporate our perceptions appropriately.

Self-Actualization

Reaching your potential can be simple or difficult depending on your state of being, awareness, and developmental growth. We must grow by achieving different levels of awareness where our needs can be meant so that we ultimately achieve our potential. A well-known psychologist was Abe Maslow who developed the hierarchy of needs for his self-actualization theory on the development of humans. He stated that we have to belong in order to be creative and reach our full potential. Other theorists believed that we didn't have to follow Maslow's hierarchy of needs in a specific order.

We have to be free to be ourselves. We have to know our needs and be willing to grow and evolve with each level of self. Maslow stated we cannot reach our full potential without our primary basic needs first. As a psychologist who studied human behavior he researched chimpanzees and their social interactions (i.e. playing, eating and grooming). Maslow's hierarchy of basic needs included all levels below self-esteem and self-actualization, such as food and safety. He states "We have to achieve the lower levels before we can fulfill our higher needs."

Below is Maslow's view of hierarchical needs starting with the lowest level:

1. Physiological Need — basic physical needs such as, thirst, food, shelter, etc. The body needs to survive the physical realm of life.

2. Safety Need — basic environmental needs such as, body temperature, emotional safety, no physical harm, etc. A person cannot be afraid to be present in a situation.

3. Belonging Need — every person needs to feel accepted and wanted in his or her immediate surroundings without feeling like an outcast.

4. Self-Esteem Need — our need to feel good about ourselves motivates us to become the best we can be through achievement and hard work.

5. Self-Actualization — we only achieve our potential after we meet our basic needs to create and become the best we can be for ultimate happiness.

Our needs can only be fulfilled when we are aware of them. We must identify exactly what we need to achieve for well-being. All the great theorists and psychologists have determined we are a product of our environment. Behavior is the result of our personality as it matures to become our unique selves.

KURT LEWIN'S THEORY

Lewin was one of the first social psychologists in the United States (first half of the last century) whose theory stated that each person exists within a "field of forces" where the individual is reacting or responding to their life experiences. This field is a "life space" where learning is relative to all the action and energy that surrounds us. Insight is gained through experience and who we are is developed from interpreting different life situations. Lewin believed that everything we experience affects our personality, behavior, and who we are, including our self-value.

He also came up with a mathematical summary of behavior which states that behavior is the product of our personality and our environment. Thus he claimed that "a dynamic balance of forces in opposing directions" is constantly reacting within an individual. Other theorists have built on his findings; however, he was the first to state that our behavior is a combination of forces from the interactions of personality and the environment. We understand this to be true and we are developing who we are from the knowledge of the forces and energies that affect us daily. We are made up of energy that we can feel and measure. We are a product of what we do, who we see, and where we are.

Happiness reflects a harmonious life when we share our joyous selves with others. The Merriam-Webster dictionary defines happiness as a "state of being free from illness, a feeling of pleasure or joy". When we find meaning in life with a clear purpose, there is a feeling of satisfaction, self-realization, and a sense of well-being. If we choose to live a life of creativity, we could be reaching our potential via all parts of self (physical, emotional, mental, and spiritual), integrating the gifts we possess. Happiness includes the mental and spiritual parts of self; social interactions focus on the emotional self; and health deals with the total self. Peace and joy are realized when all parts of self are integrated. Discovering YOU in you is a lifelong adventure.

OPTIMAL LIFESTYLE

Acknowledgment

"Love and compassion are necessities not luxuries. Without them, humanity cannot survive. Happiness is not something ready-made. It comes from your own actions... It lives inside us and we cannot find it outside of who we are...Just one small positive thought in the morning can change your whole day...Do not let the behavior of others destroy your inner peace... "

ৼ Dalai Lama

Your goal is to enlighten and raise the process of living a healthy, balanced, and peaceful life at your optimal best. Stress is your worst enemy and it exists within (worry, fear, and anxiety). You cannot be your best if subject to obstruction. You never establish harmony in this environment unless there is harmony within yourself. You cannot truly love others until you love and care for you. Knowing who you are is an ongoing thoughtful process. Understanding and acknowledging your optimal health plan leads to a sense of well-being, and ultimately happiness.

The mind, body, soul, and spirit must work together to allow each person to live a spiritual life that is stress-free and harmonious with compassion, joy and kindness. If we are not well, we are not kind or generous with our hearts. When we become sad or anxious, and in pain, or depressed, we feel that we have no answers; however, there are answers. We have to silence our minds and acquire self-awareness. The HHI book, *Living Foods for Optimum Health* describes: healthy tools (food recipes), learning how to prepare daily meals (sprouts), as well as, hygiene, massage, and hydro-therapies.

The integration of healing Eastern Arts such as, Sufi, and Chinese, helps us create an internal harmony. Eastern healing arts (Buddhism, Hinduism and Chinese TAO), are healthy practices giving us inner peace and allowing the body to heal itself. There are many types of stress that affect our emotions and spirituality; thus, exercises (breath from the belly, stretching and toning, strengthening muscles) could be applied for personal relief. These practices keep our natural balance and cleanse us. The body is a self-healing organism and if allowed, it will heal with living foods since the body craves energized nutrition. Our immune system is affected by our thoughts and feelings. Stress affects every part of us.

Dr. Powell, after many years as a NYC banking executive, author, and a university educator in psychology, relates her philosophy below:

Living stress free is a fulltime job. It not only involves knowing yourself, your likes and dislikes, but also involves keeping negative thoughts out of your awareness. Living creatively means using all of your five senses and being completely alert in the present moment. Whenever I'm out of sorts or feeling stressed, I sit down, meditate, and observe nature or paint with pastels. I find that not thinking about anything else, but only the decision to choose a color or look at a duck swimming in the lake is very calming. The creative thinking process means thinking outside of the box and rearranging our thoughts. Life is simple when you live with joy and compassion.

The process of changing from negative to positive thoughts involves being in tune with all of your senses such as feeling what you are sensing, seeing what you are looking at, and listening to what you are hearing. Creativity only occurs when you are open to new ideas and not obstructed by the old ways of thinking. Your ideas can create new components from those existing when you express yourself such as walking in nature, writing a book, or composing a song. Each endeavor is an opportunity to learn about yourself and build your confidence. Tap into your inner wisdom or guidance.

It is all up to you to keep yourself confident, happy, and in harmony. One of the key tools is to use humor in daily life. Humor involves laughing at oneself, or looking at things as if you were in a cartoon. It's fun to laugh! Through unique avenues you can find your path. Never give up on yourself, your purpose and what makes you happy. Joy is a gift that you will receive when you give freely. Never forget who you are and the love that you feel for yourself and others. Life has its ups and downs; however, knowing who and where you are allows you to successfully ride the waves.

There is internal and external stress; however if we are strong internally, the external stress can be mitigated. It keeps us from ourselves and our true potential. Stress can cause disease and keep us from contentment. Follow your heart and soul in becoming the best you can be without disorder. You must connect at first with self and then with others. Choose what you need. The healing energy is within you.

Caring for others fulfills your need for joy. We receive energy from nature when we are in harmony with earthly elements. If there is too much anger or sadness, we are not present, and we become victims of our emotions. Our soul can only survive and breathe if we are not stressed, fearful, or anxious. Below are three modalities that help us find harmony for a healthy and happy life:

I. STRESS-FREE LIFE — breathing provokes stress reduction. There are different types of breathing meditations: silent, using color or tones, guiding, with organ sounds (ohmm, haaa, shh, etc.), and imagery, using fields or mountains. The breath connects the mind and the body. Being aware of emotions while meditating is a key to well-being and spirituality. Living a life with clear intention, compassion, kindness, and love for others, aids in a spiritual life free from jealousies and judgments. Spirit and breath are the same word in Greek (pneuma). Breath is our life force and the secret to spirituality. When we live a wholesome and centered life, we are at peace.

II. CALMNESS — calmness precludes anxiety and stress; mindfulness instruction and awareness of thoughts and feelings procure balance and peace. The healing arts are tools to help individuals regulate their energy and spiritual awareness. Balance of yin and yang is crucial to well-being and awakening. We need to be aware of our needs and how they affect outcomes. Nature changes and is in harmony with us. Energy currents have upper level moves which invoke masculine energies and lower level moves which connect us to earth. By quieting the mind a few minutes, we can reflect and release. We need equal energy of yin and yang for harmony. When we are in disharmony, employ calm to get back on the path of wellness.

III. HEALTHY FOODS — using food combining rules, such as, not ingesting proteins and carbohydrates at the same time helps with digestion. Maintaining quiet when consuming food is a long time tradition. Stillness increases metabolism and improves assimilation. Practices incorporating the five senses (e.g. seeing, touching, tasting, etc.) secure our awareness; healthy diets with fresh plant food, healing herbs, pure water become our medicine. All of our practices and information are integrated to give us harmonious and stress-free lives. For example, walking a bit after meals is healthy, as Hippocrates, the Greek physician, recommended.

The process of living a stress-free, healthy, and harmonious life involves living peacefully. The HHI Life Transformation Program provides tools that foster harmony and balance, as well as educates guests on the integrative food practices. Buddha was asked "What have you gained from meditation"? He replied, "Nothing! However let me tell you what I lost: anger, anxiety, depression, insecurity, fear of old age, and death." The onus is on you; you are required to discover your needs and unveil who you really are. Meditation is the key to the soul and strengthens your inner power. Our mission is to harmonize body, mind, and spirit, via knowledge and practice.

The HHI book, *Living Foods for Optimum Health*, gives us many wonderful recipes, and information about the air we breathe, and the water we drink. Stress reduction is a natural goal. When our vital energy is blocked we need to use the available forces and energy in all living things to return us to homeostasis (balance of body and mind). We get our energy from food; therefore, the right food will work for our benefit and well-being.

It is written how the breath is the "bridge between the mind and body". Meditation and Qigong can help us formulate our bridges. Remember the interplay of yin/yang, and the psyche. Life is constantly in flux as it flows. Stress keeps us from feeling compassion and love, as well as, kindness and generosity. Qigong is a way of life and a practice that gives us the tools to keep us energized, connected, and calm.

Everyone is different; thus we have to understand deficiencies and what will bring about the change we desire. With awareness we can lose weight, balance our hormones, and bring energy back into our life. What does this mean? We have to know what appeals to our five senses so that we can be satisfied and not looking outside of ourselves for fulfillment. Once on the wellness path, keep accepting the "new you."

Living foods allow us to become more energetic and to possess an enhanced mental capacity. A diet of natural and raw living foods prolongs our lifespan and brings us optimal health. This is a challenge; however, we can select tasty and creative recipes. We can indulge, guilt-free, in our food fantasies. When comparing how you feel after eating unfired foods, to how you feel after eating prepared foods, the difference is obvious. We are now healthy and happy. Ideally garden fresh food is the optimal choice. Discovering the you in each growth level is an opportunity to embrace the "new you" via each layer uncovered.

Following are some of these Recipes from the Garden:

Organic Frozen Fruit

3 cups each of peaches, bananas, strawberries, raspberries, lemon juice, and ½ cup water. Blend and pour into cups or use champion juicer.

Swedish Beet Salad

1 beet, shredded

2 carrots shredded

2 tbsp. chopped dill

Lemon juice

2 tbsp. olive oil

Red Cabbage (steamed)

1 head of red cabbage, chopped and steamed. Then add ½ tsp. cumin and 1 tsp. dry mustard. Add lemon juice and olive oil (Stevia).

Cream of Asparagus

6 cups asparagus, chopped

2 tbsp. basil

2 cups almond milk

1 avocado

1 celery stalk

1 cup chopped onion

Place all ingredients in a blender.

Banana Strawberry Shake

2 cups frozen strawberries

3 ripe frozen bananas

¼ cup coconut water

½ tsp. vanilla extract

Blend all ingredients

Spicy Tea

Herbal – ¼ tsp. ground nutmeg, ¼ tsp. ground cinnamon, ¼ tsp. ground allspice, 1/3 cup of lemon juice, 3 cups of water, Stevia to taste.

Stuffed Baked Sweet Potatoes

4 sweet potatoes – baked until tender

Mix 2 cups broccoli florets, ½ cup chopped onion, cayenne, and chipotle.

Acorn Slices

2 Acorn squash – remove seeds, cut in slices – place in skillet.

Add 1 cup water, 1/8 tsp. cayenne, 1 tbsp. lemon juice, ¼ tsp. seaweed salt. Bake until tender. Add olive oil and Stevia to taste.

Banana Split

3 frozen bananas

3 cups almond milk

3 tbsp. almond butter

Vanilla extract

(Pineapple, mangos, figs)

Garnish with fresh fruit

Pesto Sauce

Mix 1 cup chopped basil with 2 cloves garlic, 3 tbsp. pine nuts and ½ cup olive oil in blender. Serve in small bowl.

Black Olive Sauce

Mix 2 cloves of garlic, ¼ pound of olives, 1 tbsp. chopped parsley, 1 chopped red pepper, ½ cup olive oil and cayenne to taste.

Healthy food feeds life to our bodies and souls. We need to be aware of the integration of the mind, body and spirit. Our emotions come from our thoughts and feelings; therefore, with consciousness we can secure our health, well-being and happiness. We must live a life without stress, one that feeds our soul since without harmony, there is no peace and calm. Meditation is a way of life that keeps us centered and energized. We live one breath at a time; we will survive one step at a time; and then we can be healthy and happy.

LIVING WITH ENERGY

Presence

"It is very important to generate a good attitude, a good heart, as much as possible. From this, happiness in both the short term and the long term, for both yourself, and others will come...The purpose of our lives is to be happy...Love is the absence of judgment...A calm mind brings inner strength and self-confidence, so that is very important to good health... "

⌒ Dalai Lama

Becoming healthy is our goal and entails being aware and conscious. You need to be awake so that you can reach your potential and become the best you can be. The HHI book *LifeForce* describes body balance, over 120 powerful vitamins, minerals, and natural products that strengthen the immune system. Motivation to do this can be achieved by only you; however; the energy of those who care for you can inspire you to reach your goals. You are not alone. Currently obesity is reaching outlandish figures encompassing most of our population. Our culture is stuck in prepared and addictive foods that will kill us at an early age. Being present is critical in making appropriate choices. Understand your relationship with food.

Imbalance in energy of the body can lead to emotional disharmony, manifested in anger, sadness, and fear. Merriam-Webster defines life force "as the vital creative energy that all organisms have and is responsible for their growth and evolution". The Chinese call it chi or vital energy that travels through our bodies via meridians. The

Indians call it Prana which is a conscious life force that the mind can discern. We are energy. We have this vital life force that permeates us with energy centers called chakras. They can be blocked or aligned affecting our emotional and physical well-being; therefore, we must support them and keep them tuned.

The centered self helps you be in a peaceful state. Illness is warded off by a strong person who knows that bad feelings create an unhealthy life affecting not only you but those around you. HHI has recommended a reality check for guests to ask themselves these questions: How do you really feel? Are you critical of self and others? Are you easily disappointed? Are you envious and resentful of others? Do you choose solitude over human interaction? Are you willing to change to have a happier life?

If everyone was harmonious and peaceful, there would be no wars, greed, or covert evil actions. You first have to know who you are, and then know what you need, and lastly, how to keep yourself enriched. The personal formula for health and happiness takes time, experience and action. When you pursue this, then you will be joyous. HHI describes how great the power of belief can be as a positive force, since it is a belief system that has sustained your survival. Many were told they had no future left, and each fought their plight. They overcame adversity with a powerful belief system that helped them manifest positive outcomes. They did not give up hope. They maintained their beliefs until achieving their goals.

Ken Blue is Executive Chef and invaluable member of the HHI family for the last two decades. Below describes his experiences:

It's been my honor to hold the position of Executive Chef at Hippocrates Health Institute for the past twenty years. The fulfillment of inspiring and providing the embodiment of a central ideology of Hippocrates "Let food by the medicine", is immeasurable. As I went through the Health Educator Program, I came to the realization that this program was a culmination of different aspects of my life. My grandfather owned a restaurant; my father was a doctor and my mother was a pharmacist. All of this combined with the my degree, in biology, my healing work with energy in the internal arts of qigong and tai chi came together here at Hippocrates. There are many examples and testimonies of people having miraculous healing by adopting this raw food lifestyle. There are many scientific reasons and documented benefits of the healing properties of raw, vegan healthy foods, eaten in proper combination.

Our credo at HHI "Helping People Help Themselves", or as I like to say, empowering people to live this lifestyle, is the most important aspect of my job. Sometimes people want to give me credit and say that I healed them, but I quickly respond with "You healed yourself". This is very different than normal chef responsibilities or roles. It is a surrender of the desire to impress people with culinary abilities. There is a balance of wanting them to enjoy the food and "side dishes" enough to say, "I can eat this way, I can do this."

The importance of energy work in medicine at Hippocrates is growing exponentially. In fact over the years, this inspired me to deepen my level of learning to help others and myself to greater levels of health, peace and tranquility. I became a Doctor of Medical Qigong, certified through China and the IIMQ as well as a Daoist. This provided a greater level of ability for me to help people help themselves, both in my teaching and working individually with people in the Life Transformation and Cancer Wellness Programs. People who bring peace to their life are, as some would say, on the path to bring this lifestyle to the planet.

When joyful events take place you smile and proclaim that you are happy. When travelling, it is easy to say you are happy, since every minute changes with new adventures. You are engaged in the moment while travelling, learning new things, and meeting new people. Cultures around the world claim that true happiness is found in relationships and social interactions. Some may not find joy in this;

however, happiness is a state of mind depending on the "mind", "state" or "mood" of individual personalities. For example, many people experience happiness with their pets or with their children. Everyone is different, but we also have similarities. The key is to forget the past and forgive everyone, including yourself, and move on to being who you really are in the present moment.

There is no age limit to any productive activities mentioned since our only limit is ourselves. Our attitude about age limits us; therefore, with joyous experiences we could change our minds. Intimacy requires more than sex. In fact, true intimacies in romantic relationships require other aspects such as, respect, caring, affection, cuddling, listening, companionship, and sharing experiences. Many couples stay together for over 50-60 years with the knowledge that they have shared much of their life together through many ups and downs. They would never split, even if they are not as sexual as they would like. However, this can change with awareness and open honesty to try new things.

It is important to be spontaneous for a long and healthy life. Happiness fluctuates; therefore, it is important to know where you are and your moods to regulate your happiness scale. Accept your self-power and commit to finding the power of the best in you. Commit to keeping yourself strong. There are three useful criteria to regulate yourself:

1. SELF-HARMONY includes having fun and not placing lots of stress on yourself. Being comfortable with who you are, and not doing more than you can handle. Only if you are present can you assess if you are awake. Meditate to keep yourself present and calm. Know the Krebbs Cycle (a biochemical cycle that generates energy) and how it works for you to create energy and burn fat. Being aware that your metabolic rate helps you balance your energy is important.

2. SELF-AWARENESS includes having people who care for and love you and vice versa. We all need support and want to establish long-term relationships that last through all hurdles. We have to ad-

mit if we are wrong and listen in order to grow and change behavior. Select projects and events with self and peers that mean a lot to you and never give up. Be clear in your dreams; only you can live them. Be spontaneous and open to new adventures since relationships include you first, and then the ability to share with others.

3. SELF-EFFICACY includes being clear about what upsets you and what calms you. Have an open heart and be kind to all creatures and people. Be grateful and generous since all you have cannot be taken with you in the end. Do not be attached to anything since that keeps you from freedom and exploration. Take breaks from tasks, people, or events that throw you off balance. You will become unaware of yourself or your goals. People always want to talk about their things and not yours. Listen and let them speak. Know what relaxes you and do it periodically.

The purpose of life is to bring awareness to the integration of the mind/body and spirit. Our emotions come from our brain synapses and feelings; therefore, with consciousness we can secure our health, well-being, and happiness. The role of the air we breathe, the water we drink, and the food we eat is paramount. Meditation is a way of life and a practice that gives us the tools to keep us in balance and energized. Our soul will only survive if we are not stressed or anxious. We can live a harmonious healthy life, free of illness and stress. Constant vigilance on self-management keeps us on a path towards peaceful thriving.

LIFE WITH LONGEVITY

Creativity

"I believe all suffering is caused by ignorance. People inflict pain on others in the selfish pursuit of their happiness or satisfaction. Yet, true happiness comes from a sense of peace and contentment....An open heart is an open mind."

↶ Dalai Lama

Life can be joyous and surprising, if we open to the many wonders and opportunities that await us. We cannot live in fear since we will miss whatever joy there is for us. We create our own path to wellness and where ever we are along the way, we need to enjoy each moment. Give yourself permission to divert your focus occasionally for fun and spontaneity. There are no limits. We create our own obstacles which keep us from a truly rewarding and creative life. We are entitled to be happy no matter what age we are. We have knowledge now that gives us hope to prolong life by doing the right things. When we manage ourselves, our health problems appears to be less overwhelming.

Happiness resides in the mind and evokes well-being. Bliss is a state of universal happiness and as we know so well our declaration of independence claims that we have the "right to pursue happiness". We believe happiness incorporates a practice to keep the attitude of positive thinking and well-being consistent. By living healthily and eating well without abusing ourselves, we live a limitless and ageless life. Aging is a state of mind and as long as you are alive you can be happy and calm. We need courage to pursue our dreams.

Pam had been an invaluable member of the HHI family for over fifteen years. Her contributions are described below:

> Working at Hippocrates Health Institute for over fifteen years had a powerful impact on my understanding of the mind, body, spirit connection and how each one plays an integral role in supporting transformation and healing. I began my journey at Hippocrates as a massage therapist, who specialized in Craniosacral Therapy. Here I had the honor of relating to the wisdom within the body and the many ways it holds memories, emotions and tension that within a safe space would release and elicit greater freedom and flow in the people's lives.
>
> Before long, I found that my educational background could serve the Institute as well, and I began teaching some of the classes in our Life Transformation Program. This program aims to transform. It was in this role that I developed respect for the mind's ability to support new paradigms and belief systems, as well as facilitate lasting change. As people were ignited with simple truths, their natural curiosity surfaced, and engagement with new ideas fostered a quest for life. I watched ideas and truth inspire action in the lives of HHI guests.
>
> I had the opportunity to witness people on different levels of their journey. I saw them transform their health and empower their lives as they felt safe to explore new possibilities. Contributing to holding that space has remained my priority, no matter what my role. Working at Hippocrates, I gained greater awareness of the capacity we all have to transform our lives. I witnessed the value of relationship to both self and others, and what it felt like to empower the immune system. I am eternally grateful to our gracious and courageous visionaries, Brian and Anna Maria Clement. I feel deep gratitude for the personal health, growth, and relationships that had been made possible as a result of my immersion in the holistic living foods lifestyle at Hippocrates Wellness.

If we are truly aware and awake when we are eating, our bodies will tell us what is good or bad. This is very personal and each individual has to find a way to optimize the best nutrition to keep their bodies humming with lots of energy. Our background and history, as well as our experiences contribute to this process. We can feel healthy energy when we are with healthy people. The HHI book, *Longevity: Enjoying Life Without Limits* involves three major topics depicted in fifteen chapters. These chapters help us learn how to live a happy and healthy life.

Three recommendations for happiness are listed below:

1. RELAXATION — including no stress, lots of rest, exercise and eating healthy. There is always something we can do to help us be healthy and calm. We live a stress free life if we are aware and honest within our own sense of self and well-being. Relaxing aids awareness.
2. CONTEMPLATION — breathing, listening, and living in the present moment. Positive attitudes help us maintain a state of awareness that can minimize discomfort. Addictions keep us from feeling emotions, which cut us off from living. We can live free from sabotage.
3. INTERACTIONS — connections that help us remain present and cared for with love. Pure love energy lasts forever and can never be erased. We thrive with happy memories. Being our authentic selves helps us to be real in social interactions.

The HHI book, *Longevity* gives many examples of herbal and natural remedies, as well as food choices we can choose during our daily lives. Health incorporates lovemaking as a needed drive. Intimacy can help us become healthier (physically, emotionally, mentally and spiritually). It unites two loving souls into one loving entity. This occurs when each gives freely to the other without conditions or control. A couple may be in a situation where the highest level of bliss is not oc-curring; however, this will be amplified with sharing genuine feelings.

People in marriages or partnerships whether living together or not, experience many ups and downs; however, they will never split up for fear of being alone. They may not even be as sexual as they would like to be; however, this can change with awareness and open honesty to try new things. As we age, fear of not being as we were creeps in and keeps us isolated. Once again this is limiting and not the way things have to be. Honest heart felt communication works. Courage is a necessity to keep couples together.

Lovemaking is an essential element of adult functioning, and lengthy abstinence (whether chosen or situational) depletes the strength of body and the resilience of the emotions. Unfortunately, we are plagued with problems and various physical issues when we age that prohibit or diminish our capabilities; however, cuddling is known to release the strongest hormonal love feelings. Obesity, poor nutrition, dairy, and other factors may contribute to less intimacy. Male and female problems with their sexual organs (prostrate and female sex organs) hinder sexual desire and ability. All of this is cor-rectable.

We are a product of our environment, thoughts, physical lim-itations, and emotional problems, which preclude our fully satisfied sexual union; however, touching, massage, and intimacy with eye contact diminish lonely feelings. Reading to each other, sharing poet-ry or music, can keep the embers burning. The more creative you are with sharing who you are, the more true intimacy will exist and last forever. Critical thinking and making decisions are the highest forms of intelligence. Seek approval from yourself, not from others. Be kind, grateful, happy, and blissful; which leads to grand happiness. Pure in-timacy with another is a soul-to-soul connection which is powerful and contributes to a long term relationship.

HEALTHY RECIPES

Belonging

"Happiness is when what you think, what you say and what you do are in harmony... The future depends on what we do in the present... Strength comes not from physical capacity; it comes from an indomitable will... Where there is love, there is life."

       ∽ Ghandi

Part of the challenge of living a healthy and happy life is creating recipes the nourish us and appeal to our taste buds. Food is the center of social gatherings and a healthy cuisine supports our health and happiness. In the twentieth century, the cottage industry of recipe books was organically created by companies like Betty Crocker. Many new diets have been introduced, such as, the Blood Type Diet, the Paleo Diet and the Keto Diet. These diets forged the landscapes of common beliefs about food and weight loss.

A step up from the diets previously mentioned are those that have expanded but not fully comprehended nor embraced the cutting edge science. This science has revealed that the cooking of even the best organic plant based food destroys a plethora of essential nutrients.

Most important, the phytochemicals (medicines) within food decreases heart disease, diabetes, cancer, and dementia/Alzheimer's, etc. Each new philosophy and fad presents new perplexing ideas that further capture the public's interest. All of the other billions of creatures that we share the earth with seemingly do well without diet plans and reading recipe books. They all share one common fuel source, uncooked and raw.

Our species is the only one that chooses to destroy nutrients by processing, cooking, preserving, genetically modifying, irradiating, and adding chemicals to what we consume. HHI's food preparation was born out of nature's foundational banquet and researched, prepared, adapted, and utilized here at Hippocrates Wellness, which is now in our seventh decade of service. It has a wider scope, providing an endless array of life building choices. Beyond the main courses of delectable life filled offerings. HHI offers and presents a variety of delicious treats.

The way most of us eat and the choices we make are molded by an interaction of neurochemicals, nutritional, cultural, and psychological belies. You can alleviate destructive habits by satiating your body with pure, delightful, organic splendors. We need to navigate the healthiest combinations of life enhancing, longevity creating cuisine. Hippocrates master chefs, offer the core substance of living a rich plant based life in the book Healthful Cuisine. Dr. Anna Maria Clement's recipes are considered some of the most creative and nutritionally satisfying in the world.

The secret to happiness is to be authentic. Figure out what it is that makes you balanced and emotionally centered. We forget to breathe deeply which helps us be steady and calm. The mind is subject to thoughts, feelings, and physical bodily conditions. With love, care, kindness, and generosity we are reminded to take care of ourselves, as well as others. Everyone is unique; therefore, create your own lifestyle. Be honest and you will succeed.

The HHI book, *Healthful Cuisine,* inspires artistry in raw food cuisine, and describes setting up a raw vegan kitchen employing juicers, blenders and dehydrators. There is even a special chapter dedicated to the many uses of avocados in recipes such as, soups, meals, and desserts. This comprehensive A-Z book depicts kitchen equipment, tantalizing recipes, soups, sauces, and desserts. The illustrations provide vibrant pictures to guide you along the way. It is an important educational food companion.

We have selected our favorite recipes to open your eyes to the endless potential that awaits you. Get ready to explore the taste filled nutritious splendor of raw foods. The recipes will help you eat a healthy lifestyle that is delicious and easy to prepare.

Below are some examples of HHI recipes:

Cucumber Soup

2 lb. cucumber, peeled, halved

½ cup chopped yellow onion

1 cup almond milk and almond butter

Place in blender until smooth. Serve with chopped scallions, red peppers, dill, and seaweed. Salt to taste.

Butternut Squash Soup

1 butternut Squash, chopped

In food processor:

1 tsp sage,

Chopped onion

1tsp. chipotle

1 celery, chopped

2 carrots, chopped

3 cups of juice (½ celery, ½ cucumber) add oil to taste and seaweed salts.

Alternative Butternut Squash Soup

Cut squash in half; skin the squash, scoop out seeds. Steam or bake. Seaweed salt to taste.

Blend with 2 cups almond milk, coriander, cinnamon, cayenne pepper and ginger to taste.

Garnish with chopped nuts and cilantro, 1 tbsp. of sesame or olive oil, and grated nutmeg.

Snow Peas with Leek Soup

2 leeks

1lb. of snow peas

Blend with juice from cucumber and celery – 3 cups + ½ cup almond milk 2 tbsp. almond batter or avocado, and 1tsp of tarragon.

Fennel Salad

1cup sliced fennel (very thin, from the center)

1 cup mesclun

1 cup arugula

Thinly sliced almonds

Asian Mung Bean

3 tbsp. of lime juice

A few drops of Stevia to taste

3 tsp. of sesame oil

3 garlic cloves

1 jalapeno

1 small piece of ginger

1 sliced cucumber

2 cups shredded carrots

3 chopped scallions

4 cups of mung beans

Olive Paste

½ cup pitted Kalamata olives

1 tbsp. chopped onion

Pinch of thyme

1 tbsp. olive oil

Juice of lemon to taste

Chick Peas

1 cup of chick peas, soaked overnight, sprouted for 24 hrs. Boil beans until soft. Drain.

Add:

1 clove of garlic

1 tsp. of cumin

½ tsp. of paprika

1 tsp. of lemon juice

10 Kalamata olives

Red peppers

Cilantro

Happiness

½ onion chopped

1 cup dill or thyme

2 cups arugula

Sauce:

½ cup pine nuts

¼ cup almond milk

1 tbsp. olive oil

1 tbsp. lemon juice

Place ingredients in food processor and puree until smooth with cilantro and garlic.

Cilantro Red Pepper Salsa

2 cups cilantro

¼ tsp. cayenne

1 tbsp. lemon juice

1 tbsp. grated peel of lemon

2 cloves of garlic

Cumin to taste

4 tbsp. of olive oil

Seaweed salt to taste

Blend, pour over chopped red peppers

Pine Nut Dressing

½ cup pine nuts

¼ cup almond milk

Lemon juice

Cayenne

Olive oil

Blend until smooth.

Pickled Onion

1 red or yellow onion

1 cup water

Stevia

Marjoram

Cut onion into rounds, separate; lemon or lime juice. Let sit overnight.

Parsley Salad

3 cup chopped parsley

Marjoram

Chives or scallions

1 tbsp. thin round sliced radish

1 tbsp. olive oil (1 lemon juice)

Spinach Salad

1 bunch fresh spinach – rinse and cut

1 cup sliced shitake mushrooms

2 scallions, chopped

1 ½ cup walnuts

2 tbsp. olive oil

1 tbsp. lemon juice

Many guests have come to HHI and captured the essence of themselves by putting their health first. The first step is to be in charge of your life. It is important to be spontaneous for a long and healthy lifespan. Happiness fluctuates; so you need to learn how to know where you are, your moods, and your feelings at any given time. Overwhelming emotions can deter you from clear thinking. Become aware, and if your health becomes compromised take action. The preparation and consumption of healthy vital food is paramount and gives us happiness through energy. Believe you can do this and you will discover the gift of health, happiness, and healing within you.

EMOTIONAL ENERGY

Spirituality

"True knowledge exists in knowing that you know nothing....To find yourself, think for yourself... I cannot teach anybody anything; I can only make them think...I ask them questions...True wisdom comes to each of us when we realize how little we understand about life, ourselves and the world around us."

∽ Socrates

Understanding our spiritual needs fosters our emotional energy and vitality. Emotions are the non-verbal language that is the most truthful and the most misunderstood. Emotions are feelings and they are our way of communicating what we internalize. Sometimes we are sad or joyful and we will act accordingly. If we suppress our emotions we are susceptible to addictions; thus, we need a healthy way of dealing with them. In order to be happy, it is important to recognize emotions and deal with them realistically. Keep yourself in acceptance mode and not in expectation which can lead to resentment, disappointment, and frustration.

The HHI book *Emo-Spirit*, depicts how the emotions influence our spiritual depth. Being spiritual implies relating to sacred matters or rules that help you gain a higher level of self that is not mired by the mundanities of ordinary life. By becoming spiritual and employing your higher self and potential or self-actualized self you have a path to joy. Only by raising yourself from the petty lifestyle of arguments, jealousies, envies, and dishonest connections can you maintain a happy life. This helps maintain your confidence. Handling fear is helpful to prevent self-sabotage.

Confidence comes and goes as does happiness, thus, it is evident how important it is to be totally in the present moment to discover your needs. The self contains physical, emotional, mental, and spiritual needs. Commitment, self-knowledge, and willingness to make the right choices that benefit you, are all required. If you are off balance, you might make decisions that are not in your best interest. When you are aware of your natural state at any given point in time, you become more spiritual and happy. You can do this by just being conscious and aware of your feelings, beliefs, and actions.

The minute you get yourself on purpose, and focused, you become confident and centered. When in the zone and in the present moment, confidence affects what you are doing and elevates your accomplishments. You must give yourself healthy food to survive and find clarity of perception to discover YOU.

The HHI book *Emo-Spirit,* gives you the background for understanding what hinders you from becoming your highest potential or the best you can be. The following are five aspects for freedom:

1. Consciousness is required to allow your true feeling of self to flourish. We can only help ourselves if we are awake and aware of who we are and what we need.

2. Our spiritual self is held back by our emotional self. Emotions are a reflection of our spiritual depth and we need to acknowledge them to achieve well-being.

3. Childhood could have hurt and bruised us as we experienced growing in an environment that may not have been the best. We should not let these hurts hold us back.

4. We have to escape the chains of the mind and free our spirit which is held back by our thoughts and doubts of who we are. We need to be our true selves.

5. Our emotional and spiritual selves need to get together and work together to let us become our best. We cannot afford bickering between spirit and emotion.

Emotions reflect what we think and they express our strong feelings. We are all gifted so we need to enrich ourselves to become passionate and creative. Relationships are important for consistent happiness. Listening skills (flow of energy) in relationships are important for connections to manifest and to exist. Connections are fluid and some are temporary while others are maintained throughout life. The five following events contribute to better relationships and human connections:

1. A SENSE OF SELF — Listening is important for any connection to exist and especially listening to oneself before you can listen to another. This requires that you must practice main-

taining high self-esteem, mindfulness, and presence. Self-respect is required to be honest with yourself.

2. CONFIDENCE — True confidence involves active participation in building your self-confidence. To be present means to be active and knowing your capabilities. Mastering connections with confidence must precede relationships for true sharing. You have to maintain our self-confidence since it fluctuates and requires presence.

3. PRESENCE — Accepting that you exist as a complete person in the present moment. This is accomplished through practice and meditation. If you are worried constantly, anxious, or in fear then you are not available. If you are sad and grieving, you are elsewhere, then you are in the past and missing out in the present moment.

4. SHARING — Authenticity and sharing can only occur if two or more people are connected in the present moment with a similar vision. You have to be who you really are to connect heart and soul with someone else. Honesty is vital and without it the connection falls apart. Deep honesty is the glue.

5. COURAGE — Fearlessness within a person must involve courage. You may become a victim by accepting judgment and experiencing hurt. To truly connect, judgment must be let go, as well as comparing oneself to others or feeling envious. You are a beautiful and unique person without having to be compared to others. Be who you are, everyone else is already taken.

People render up images where elation and joy reign when recalling the light and fulfilling senses of happy events. Seldom do we meet someone that lives and thinks in the now, experiencing a fully joyous and unequivocally free life. Seemingly we have all settled for far less than the promise that life offers. As children, our natural way is to employ expansive imagination and a happy-go-lucky existence. Imaginary friends and acceptance from and of others are the hallmark for most children. Our young rarely judge and freely love. To become skeptical requires experiences that provoke fear and protection of what you perceive you possess.

Accumulating restrictiveness limits progress and squelches authenticity. Why so many people find themselves lonely is that their armor is too thick to permeate. They cannot express themselves fully because of the hurt that they carry from days gone by. In addition, we live in a culture that revels in the negative and elevates discord to the level of a sporting event. Many people would rather engage in conflict then embrace resolution. Ultimately each of us projects our truest person through our emotional and physical actions. Wayne Dyer said: "When you squeeze an orange, orange juice comes out". The same holds true for us. When we are squeezed, what is inside comes out. This is a great reminder to observe our reactions and work on what we want to be on the inside so others will see it.

Joy is wonderful when we share who we are with others. Bliss is the highest level of happiness and can occur individually or with a group. Meditation helps us stay in the present moment. Breathing is important to ground us. Breath does not lie. When we hear or know our thoughts and feelings they will tell you the truth. Be open and aware of this process. Be truthful and know reality. We will be happy when we do not compare the self to others. Everyone must find a personal formula that fits.

Who we are is affected by lifestyle, background, genetics, and our social contacts and environment. An individual is made up of many parts of self which ancient theorists (such as Plato and Aristotle) have defined as "the actual self" or the "ideal self". Other theorists have defined it as the "true self or the false self". There are many variables that influence the self. One's background and family upbringing are important in the initial stages of defining who we are. When we discover who we are we can accept ourselves and continue our journey.

CHANGING PASSAGES

Adaptability

"If thou findest in human life anything better than justice, truth, temperance, fortitude, and anything better than thy own mind's self-satisfaction in the things which enables them to do accordingly to right reason...turn to it with all thy soul, and enjoy that which thou hast found to be the best...we only live in the present."
     ∽ Marcus Aurelius

Nothing is permanent in life. The ability to adapt to life-changing challenges is a required skill. As new events occur, we must accept and adapt them to our purpose. In the latter part of life, both men and women face changing parts of self. (physical, emotional, mental) which can surprise them. As we go through life's experiences, we adapt using various coping skills as defense mechanisms, such as denial. At times, we need to adjust to life's overwhelming challenges by distinguishing reality from illusion. When aware, we tend to be honest and know what obstacles prevent us from accepting reality.

As males age, they may not be prepared with the skills necessary to travel the passages of time. Each decade will bring changes as young adults mature. The HHI book *Man-Opause* describes in a holistic and scientific manner, male hormonal imbalance, symptoms, and navigation of bodily changes. This is a start for understanding the latter years of manhood, in order to cope with changes that minimize symptoms, such as low testosterone, obesity, and fears of losing man-hood.

During male menopause some men complain about chronic fatigue, sleep disorders, and mood changes. A few men are concerned about bone and joint degeneration, as well as loss of hair. Solutions may include lifestyle changes, hormone replacement therapy, and phytochemical supplementation. When undergoing life changes, acceptance is preferable rather than denial or escapism.

Denial is a defense mechanism and action that declares what we experience as untrue. We ignore the reality of the situation in order to avoid pain, anxiety, and disappointment. Many people use elaborate strategies to protect themselves and cope with the stressful feelings ,such as, not acknowledging truth.

Dr. Powell's esteemed colleague and friend, Paul Greco, was a mechanical designer and inventor. He produced volumes of technical tools and has spent many years understanding human behavior. His studies include emotional health and he supports many people in discovering and understanding themselves. Below are his comments on denial:

> Through personal experience and way too much time living on this planet, I have come to believe a few things about the concept of denial. I believe denial to be an evolutionary trait which has helped we humans survive and thrive. As with all evolutionary traits, this can be useful, but also has the potential to cause more than a few problems at some point of practice. For example: A real estate developer announces a plan to build a 40-story mixed-use high-rise building. He claims this will be a wonderful project. The city will be very excited to have it and will give its approval handily. He adds the construction industry will benefit industry will benefit greatly with jobs for everyone. The financial community will fully endorse and create the necessary funding to make it all possible. The citizens of our Fair City will love it and everyone will benefit.

Truth or fiction? Only time will tell. Whether these claims come to pass or were a complete denial of reality are what would be considered necessary in order to entertain the possibility of undertaking this project. I believe without the basic human capacity to see reality in the way they would like it to be, nothing would ever be accomplished.

When does this become a barrier rather than a stepping stone? In our earlier example one would hope there was a complete examination of these risks and realities; however, at some point unknown possibilities arise. Denial can mean accepting false premises as truth or even escaping from reality.

There are many categories and reactions to denial depending on events. I would like to examine how a similar dynamic might enter into what could be called psychological denial, where the focus of such denial is projected onto known facts, behavior, or perceptions of past events. We find ourselves in predicaments that are hard to handle and perceive; thus we deny that they exist. Denial is an attempt to cope, rationalize, or excuse behavior. Below are denial categories and real life experiences:

Categories of Denial

- Self-denial (to protect the ego from difficult events
- Factual denial (to not accept reality and facts become illusion
- Events denial (to see events unreal and unrecognizable)
- Verbal denial (to hear words that are rationalizations to support denial)
- Crazy making denial (to make untrue proclamations such as blame and guilt)

How can this distortion of one's reality affect an individual's quality of life? Which endeavors such as personal accomplishments and relationships are affected? Can we determine how different levels and types of denial affect all aspects of life experiences?

Relationships:

- Narcissism (exaggerated sense of self-importance and lacking empathy)
- Self-centered (not listening to others and ignoring their needs)
- Controlling (manipulating people and decisions)

Self-perception:

- Confidence (feeling self-assured and appreciating your own ability)
- Self-esteem (confidence in one's own worth and self-respect)
- Humility (modesty and taking care of others)

World view:

- Rationality (based on reason or logic, sensible and intelligent)
- Truth seeking (honesty and asking challenging questions)
- Honesty (integrating trustworthiness, loyalty, and sincerity)

Accomplishments:

- Generosity (the quality of being kind, playful, and happy to give to others)

- Compassionate (feeling sympathetic and showing care for others)
- Spiritual (affecting human spirit and soul)
- Non-egocentric (people's inability to understand another's view)

Once you create your own formula for success, you have to learn how to maintain it or else you fail. Start by finding what's important to you and focusing on your goals in sight. Be truthful with personal events and avoid denial or delusion. Avoid stress and polluting sustenance. You are in charge of fulfilling your health needs. Follow the suggestions listed below:

1. Identify your preferred foods and what are the beneficial options for you. Once you know the right combination of foods, you are on your way to health.

2. Acknowledge your five senses (eyesight, touch, hearing, smell, and taste) and what appeals to you personally from your own background and experiences.

3. Figure out what level of energy you have and which foods are best for you. Living foods react differently for each person and always open the flood gates.

4. Pick food choices based on your needs (physical, emotional, mental, and spiritually). We all need comfort foods but this does not mean that they can't be healthy choices.

5. Find food recipes to create your own formula based on your requirements for health and what gives you the most enrichment. Explore and be open.

Once you make a commitment to live a healthy lifestyle, you have embarked on a road to discovery that encompasses your physical, emotional, and spiritual needs. Choices affect your health each day of your life. This task can be overwhelming, and sometimes when changing old habits, it any be daunting and terrifying. Choose the techniques and information you need to make your path to well-being easier. Be open to self-discovery.

This is your journey to health and path to happiness. This process depends on your commitment. Each selection needs to support your personal goals. You are now prepared and confident to achieve health, happiness, and calm. The health and happiness journey requires honesty, focus, and determination.

BLISSFUL HAPPINESS

Additional Stories

Happiness is not just about being joyous for a few hours, but rather living a lifetime with high ideals. When reaching bliss (comprehensive happiness) we are in a state of elation and not affected by negative environments. The goal of happiness has been pursued for millennea. The philosopher Aristotle (fourth century B.C.) said: "Happiness is the meaning and purpose of life, the whole aim to the end of human existence. Happiness depends on us and the culture we embrace." We can learn from ancient philosophers since their wisdom is still applicable today

According to Aristotle, happiness is living a good and noble life with strong moral, and rational principles while pursuing intellectual curiosity. When reaching our full potential, we meet the best of human nature which includes generosity, kindness, compassion, and virtuous goals. We need to listen to our hearts and learn from the behavior of others.

Stories about people's personal experiences help us with our own journey. Everyone's story always has an "aha" moment or an awakening when they realize who they are. They learn from their assets and defects, which may lead to revelation. Investment in finding who we really are allows us to live happily and with purpose. Happiness is prevalent in self-realized individuals. Knowing and understanding our life's purpose is a result of honest self-evaluation with integrity. Our culture needs to change and we must focus on personal development, rather than looking for joy outside of ourselves.

Imagine a world where all people are at peace, wanting the best for themselves and others, and recognizing the awesome responsibility they have to spread love. All of our manufactured problems would be washed away and a new sense of optimism and progress would begin to flow. There are many guests here at HHI Wellness who become more like family, as they continue to follow the lifestyle and share the best of who they are.

Jarod, who is a loyal HHI friend has an unbreakable spirit. He is 100 percent committed to maintaining a lifestyle of health and happiness. He shares his story:

Growing up was pretty typical: I was born in New York, and had loving parents who both smoked incessantly. When I went to college, I realized after a year that I wanted to become an entrepreneur and started my own wholesale business in 1980. The wholesale food business in Long Island New York included selling to restaurants, catering halls, and schools. This was a high stress environment with eighteen-hour days. I was challenged with extending credit for perishable commodities.

Minimal happiness and work, culminated in an attack in 1986, which turned out to be Multiple Sclerosis. I was 29 years old. A few years before the initial attack, I met a beautiful woman and marriage was in the cards. I knew she was the right one and we got married in 1988. We decided we'd retire to Florida but I was concerned about MS and possibly not surviving. That conversation led me to sell my business and move. I quickly learned that MS hampers cognitive function and thus I had multiple jobs. We were blessed with fraternal twins. Unfortunately our marriage did not last and we divorced.

My neurologist put me on several drugs and I stopped them in 2008. In 2010 I was blessed with a new partner and her care for me got me through hard years. In 2009 I became a vegetarian. I continued my diet over the next three years with a positive attitude. In 2012 I had my birthday dinner at HHI. I was amazed upon my arrival at the beautiful bouquet of food and knew at first bite I was going vegan. In 2013 I adopted the lifestyle and was able to walk twenty feet on my own after only twelve days. I was totally committed to health and success.

I embraced the fact that "no health, no happiness" was intertwined with "no happiness, no health"; thus my life became amazing. At 65, my energy makes it difficult for my partner to keep up and I attribute this to my sprouts and the HHI lifestyle. I continue living a very active lifestyle working out three or four days a week and attending concerts, as well enjoying dinner and movies. I've been asymptomatic for the last nine years and I am living and loving my life. I have been told by medical experts that I am the only person alive on earth who not only survived but thrived with this disorder. I have MS; however, MS does not have me. In my mind, it's gone.

We all want friends, partners, and community. Yet very few of us put the time and effort into being successful in relationships. Most of this stems from what we learned in the developmental years between conception and six years of age. As researchers explain, all but fifteen percent of our personalities are developed during this tender time. If we had abusive parents and a disharmonious family. All of this is often compounded with a lack of economics and/or food; this will inevitably skew our perception. Others may have had the gift of loving and supportive parents and the comfort of a secure, stable childhood. We never had a formal education on relationships; therefore, we must learn on our own.

Even western medicine has accepted acupuncture which moves energy throughout the body, and helps balance the mind and heart. We have the essential task of formulating a centered and aligned existence. We must aspire to be aware and emotionally harmonious in all situations at all times. Everyone can do this since there is no limit.

Below are practices to help cultivate your personal formula:

1. BE GENEROUS. You need to be giving to others, since when you are self-involved and only think of yourself, you will not find peace. You will be wondering why you are sad.

2. BE GENUINE. You need not be superficial or deceptive to yourself or others. When you lie you contaminate and build illness in your heart and spirit that is detrimental.

3. BE GRATEFUL. You need to be thankful and accepting of all that is part of you, considering that things are the way they are for a reason. Let go and be with the flow.

4. BE CONFIDENT. You can only be happy if you feel you are able to do things well. Accomplishing endless success gives you the ability to repeat it and achieve it again, resulting in confidence.

5. BE CONSIDERATE. You can only be centered if you are

aware of yourself and your feelings. When you are kind to others, you mutually share your hearts.

6. BE CONNECTED. You need to share your compassion with family, friends, coworkers and all of humanity. If disconnected you are not present and not congruent.

7. BE FREE. Your spirit needs to soar and only if unencumbered by sadness and future worries can you feel ready and strong to accomplish what you need.

8. BE FRIENDLY. You need to feel kind to self and others since if negative feelings surface you are disconnected with your higher purpose and you tend to lack wellness.

9. BE FOCUSED. You need to be clear and ready to be in harmony. When you allow yourself to disconnect from the present, confusion reigns and focus wans.

10. BE PURPOSEFUL. You need to know what you want in life and what you need since that is the way to be powerful and effective. If unsure, you will miss your goals and flounder.

11. BE PRESENT. You cannot know what you need unless you assess where you stand, by harvesting the moment. Aspire to think, live, and be present always.

12. BE PEACEFUL. Your essence of well-being depends upon composure, clarity, and calm. Turmoil and emotional violence wreak havoc and steal your soul and focus. Be calm.

The above twelve practices are there to remind you of how tenuous health and well-being can be and any kind of ill will create disharmony. Once happiness is achieved with awareness, then bliss or spiritual elevation will be reached, as well as, joy in the heart.

Many of us have tried hard to gain acceptance from peers and have fallen short. Others have been bullied and unjustly treated. All seems hopeless until you realize that there are people who dismissed their problematic past and replaced it with a passionate, purposeful future. Brian relates one of his experiences:

Years ago, I became familiar with a man who had formerly been a drug addict. He clawed his way out of the grips of this disease and later became a facilitator for a motivational group. Continually he asked me to join him at one of his events and I kept making excuses until he finally found out that the engagement I had claimed was fabricated. Wisely, he said, "I'll pick you up on Friday night, be prepared to spend all weekend until late Sunday and I promise you will be a different man when you return". Frankly out of guilt, my wife and I submitted to his request and reluctantly we awaited this upcoming adventure. Once we arrived, we began the process with a small group and by 10:30pm that evening we were fully engaged. There were many tears and bursts of joy but one thing I was sure of, this kind and brilliant man was one of the best teachers I'd ever encountered.

His unadulterated honesty and sense of integrity governed the culture and spirit during the entire weekend. We, who thought we lived perfectly happy lives, slowly began to recognize that we too were harboring discontent and even anger. Like unloading a truck, as we drove down this 30-hour road, we lightened our cargo. By late Sunday, we were doing everything in our power not to be singing out loud and dancing around the room. Reflecting upon what I now perceive as one of the highlights of a long life with many spikes of greatness, this was one of the foremost altering experiences I've had.

What was it about him that made it so easy for us to gain confidence and trust? Surely it was his own transformation from a pessimist to an illuminant. He had broken down into a basic level, and reconstructed his life to a magnificent place. For him it was easy to see through the shallow veneers that each participant wore. He most likely resonated with this because he had been a serial self-loather himself. It was natural for him to help us pull the discord out of our bodies and minds.

Charismatic movements, gospel churches, and even fans at a successful sport's team event, symbiotically raise each other out of a malaise to the heightened level of unity that all should experience. Relationships are the purpose for human existence. We are not solo acts but rather choruses that together create the beautiful melody of reality. Successful relationships lead to a harmonious lifestyle where partners share their inner most thoughts, feeling safe and free. Our presence in social interactions can lead us to meaningful relations, stability, and happiness.

There is no doubt that we all have a lot of work to do on ourselves so that we are desirable as a friend, mate, coworker, or neighbor. Most of us have experienced that remarkable person in our lives who was so loved that we are elated when we see them. They may exude positive vibes, yet it is our desire to be infected by their irresistible or contagious energy that attracts us. Seemingly, we all crave being close to the newly born since they are energetically irresistible. There is a systematic way to start down the road by demolishing the barricades and replacing them with possibilities. Granted, it is a fearsome project that requires complete focus and trust. This is not something that can be done at night or on the weekends, but rather requires a 365 day commitment, and then, more and more.

Moving from the acceptance of failure to the intolerance of anything but joy can iron out all personality flaws. Each of us has an inherent ability to supersede the problematic patterns that have been etched out over a lifetime of discontent. Resolution, as difficult as it appears, takes only one courageous act called forgiveness. When submitting to this obvious tool, you will instantly feel the release of sorrow and the room to grow. We can fulfill our lives with mutual experiences, when sharing with others who we authentically are.

A mature HHI guest wrote a letter to his wife in his diary as a means of expressing his feelings about their relationship. Below is an honest evaluation of his life that he wrote after attending Hippocrates:

I think that we need to rethink our relationship. It's very clear to me that we are not on the same page and moving in the same direction.

From my perspective the energy that bound us together over the years was founded first on creating a strong family unit and secondly, a successful legacy business. For years we worked as a team to create a fabulous son, Sandy. As we both know we had an amazing adventure in Colorado and we lived our dreams. It was clearly the best twenty-plus years of my life. We were galloping on horses over the meadows, riding dirt bikes and snowmobiles, gazing over the mountain views with colorful Alpine Glow, going to the rodeos, wearing cowboy hats and country dancing, etc. On top of that we had amazing trips to several continents like, Africa and South America. Yet that all came to an end and the energy moved on as Sandy grew up, graduating from college and thus, we truly became empty nesters.

For close to nine years we have all worked non-stop to protect the Company: First from the competitive threats of other companies and most recently from global economic concerns. Even though the company still has challenges, it appears to be on a very solid foundation due to everyone's hard work.

It's at this point that the energy that has always bound us together is starting to diverge. Over the last six months I made the decision to begin transitioning out of our company to have our son take over. It seemed to be the best path to make it possible for Sandy to assume the mantle without my undue influence. It has worked well to date; however, I am always available for his council.

The three weeks at Hippocrates was the perfect time for me

to take a personal inventory. In fact, it was the first time in my life that I was alone for three weeks to do as I pleased. Every choice and decision I made was all my own and not subject to someone else's perspective. Furthermore all the feelings and emotions that I experienced were all my own, whether from my actions or shadows from the past. All of my demons that reared up were all personal, of my own doing; whether it was the fear of failure, abandonment, loneliness, etc.

The freedom to truly experience myself in a very safe, nurturing place like Hippocrates was amazing. Whether I wanted to drink wheat grass, have a colonic, go for a workout, take a sauna, have a nap, or whatever, was all my choice. I was truly living my life as how I wanted to for that brief three week stay. For three weeks I freely made choices without listening to all the 'Shoulds' that have ruled my life. It was very refreshing and enlightening.

Over my stay, I also took inventory of my life, regarding what has worked and what has not. I realized that I have exceeded all of my expectations when it comes to my family and business. I am the dad of an amazing son, Sandy, largely due to your guidance. There is not a better parent that I know than you; you truly have a gift. Every day I wake up and thank God for picking me to be Sandy's dad.

Now that Sandy has grown up and I have stepped away from our company, I realized during my stay at Hippocrates that I needed to focus on Spiritual Growth and Inner Personal Peace. These are two areas that need my energy and focus. We all know that I have a collection of demons and shadows that continue to haunt me; whether it be the fear of failure, rejection, loneliness, etc. I think deep down it is all founded on a lack of Self-Love and Acceptance which is all a fallout from my past. I think my quest for a spiritual connection and inner peace are closely linked. How to find my way is my Big Challenge. There doesn't seem to be a simple roadmap; it's more like a journey to the unknown. I will only know that I have arrived when I arrive.

Right now I do not think that we have a lot of energy that is holding us together. The time and focus on Sandy and the company is waning. He's on his way to getting married and taking over the business. From one perspective it is 'Mission Accomplished'. From another, it's where do we go from here. It's clear to me that we both have to reinvent ourselves as this chapter in our lives comes to a conclusion. First we both have to build new connections in Upstate New York with family, friends and activities. The memories and dreams of Colorado are behind us.

We are blessed and hopeful that our paths may merge again in the future. Thanks for the time and freedom to find the answers to my questions that create the restless energy within me. As agreed, I will only return if I am 100 percent committed to our relationship where you are the one, and only one, that I choose to spend the next chapters of our lives.

Harboring pain in an unenlightened society has been glorified as a character builder. In reality, you cannot erect a strong person when a person's mind and body are filled with constant discord. Being willing to let go allows you to truly grow. Once you start experiencing fruitful rewards of expanded joy, you will rekindle a powerful level of focus. Time passing with this new found sense of confidence allows you to move peacefully and naturally through each day of your life. There is never a concern that is too large to navigate and conquer. Belief in self, determines the outcome of any venture.

How odd it is that many people entertain themselves by getting high on some form of drug. Be it alcohol or narcotics or sugary food. The very act of indulging in such disruptive behavior is a clear indication that they are not content with the life that they have formed. Instead they are running from it for a momentary reprieve. Furthermore, we have an allopathic "health care" system that prescribes psychiatric medicines for a plethora of non-related concerns.

Brian relates his meeting with a gentleman at HHI:

> Recently, I worked with a man who spent his first 30 years addicted to a wide variety of substances. After decades of abuse his heart gave out and he suffered a major coronary event. While he lay there on a respirator he paused and for the first time awoke from what he describes as a lifelong coma. Recognizing that a medical emergency occurred, what flashed through his mind initially was, "Good it's the end". In a moment of clarity, he now felt a desire to live. Entering Hippocrates was like coming to a new world for him. Every day he would repeat, "I've never felt so much love." After listening to him for three weeks we finally sat down and privately spoke. He thanked so many people here at the Institute and went on about how much they gave to him. Finally I intervened and explained what had occurred. He dropped his guard and was himself finally reflecting his true persona. It took a near death experience for him to desire life.
>
> In my work I have been blessed to counsel thousands of people in the same circumstance. What they have taught me is the preciousness of each and every day. There is always endless opportunity to achieve high aspirations that fill your heart and soul with love. Truly, strength does not come from anger; it comes from this geyser of goodness within. Throughout history we have seen multitudes of examples where the power of love has washed away the most gruesome tyranny. There was a Hitler, but there also was a Schindler. There was a Patton but there also was a Thoreau. There was a George IV but there also was a Gandhi. In every case, love precipitated historic progress and inevitably disengaged the disharmony of fear.

Discovering YOU in You is a process of exploration and willingness. You have to adapt to the curve balls in life. Each day, you should enroll yourself in the practice of acceptance; it is not a sign of weakness but rather a sign of consciousness. When we are passengers on the train of perpetual promise, we become part of the resolution. What it is that all of us need to resolve is our lack of commitment to normalcy? Although it may appear insurmountable at times, once you are focused, you will navigate and fly over even the largest barrier. Truly, the only obstacle is you.

Reaching your potential or becoming your true creative self will happen when different conflicting aspects of self-aligning and atuning passion will elevate personal strength. Thoughts and feelings work together as a whole, and are integrated by not being torn apart by conflict; they are united by a common goal which is to express and connect with oneself, surroundings, and other people.

If you are not uncentered, you will not feel well and you will not be yourself. When you are harmonious, you are happy. This means peaceful and heartfelt feelings that overcome you, as if you are in love. Only more permanent, since now you are in love with your true self. You are in the world with nature and fellow human beings. Finding who you are is the number one goal to becoming an integrated, happy and healthy self forever. There are no limits. Age is not a limit. There are no excuses. Be happy and live a long life.

There are five principles below that correlate to self-discovery:

1. AWARENESS — being awake as to who you are and what you are doing or thinking/ boundaries with self & others / self-discipline/self-love/sensitivity and awareness of self and others. Finding who you are is key to reach a peaceful and self-accepting mode. Being real with yourself is a hard quest since denial & fear exist. Be aware of your strength, confidence, and power.

2. SOCIAL CONNECTIONS — know boundaries/supportive relationships/authentic self to have honest & rewarding rela-

tions /don't lose self in relations & manage emotions / sensitivity on what hurts you/ all pain from others controlled by your attitude. People feel good when you are kind; and it is reciprocated. Be prepared not to lose yourself in the shuffle. Feelings are governed by your own attitude.

3. CREATIVITY — live with the best of yourself in the realm of creativity, which includes the ability to problem-solve and make decisions. Creation involves project management to create books, art or dance. Be open to new discoveries of self and work with others by being present without ego. Inaction breed's depression and a dull life. Be open to new ideas.

4. PASSION — living with passion and empathy for others creates a passionate and authentic lifestyle. Know what you love to do, what turns you on and how to change as new passions come into your life. Love is the most precious of human emotions. Be aware of your emotions and feelings, and do whatever it takes to keep negativity away.

5. SPIRITUALITY — living a calm life, without fear and worry about the future helps you accept others. Know your sensitivity and manage emotions. Be aware of your boundaries and don't lose yourself in doing more than you can handle. Know your peaceful quotient. MEDITATE DAILY. Value simplicity and divert fear. Be secure with yourself, and let go of stress.

Beware of aging concerns which includes keeping your mind active, knowing nutrition and the importance of hydration. Many people after middle age are faced with arthritic and joint issues, respiratory, allergies, and heart (cardiovascular) concerns, as well as cognitive problems. The average seventy-year-old consistently takes five pharmaceutical medicines. One purpose of this book is to de-myth the old adages, such as life is over after we reach middle age. The opposite is true since we are really limitless in our ability to keep feeling and enjoying life till it is over. Our soul can only survive if we are not stressed or anxious. We can live a healthy life free of illness and a life balanced in our needs, if we are aware of our internal power.

Inspiration can come from within or from the outside such as, a walk in the park, a trip to a museum or movie that totally immerses us into a world out of ourselves. We can look back and fit who we are into appropriate alignment by ridding ourselves of deception and fearful thoughts. Our complete self is integrated and totally present allowing our core self to be strong, creative and effective. Emotions are indicators of our spirituality. We can be our best.

To live blissfully involves focusing on what gives us energy and being able to lift up others. Living a meaningful and purposeful life detracts from living a self-centered life. Bliss is characterized with love, joy, forgiveness, understanding, compassion, humility, and harmony with self and others. Bliss is not about material accomplishment, but more about spiritual values where the best of self can reside in a happy place. Who can we really be? Does this change with time? The power of you is in you and only you can develop it.

Discovering YOU in You can lead to ultimate joy. How safe do we need to feel to allow who we really are to come into view? What inspires us to stop ruminating and take action as confident and effective individuals who can create and achieve our goals? Our design in life is to answer these questions and to create a life that is healthy and happy. The discovery of YOU in you involves becoming healthy, happy, and developing successful interactions. Your will, honesty, and perseverance will propel you to reach the best of you. The key to your success is truthfulness; healing only works with truth. You can heal if you are real.

Section III

INTERACTIONS

JOYOUS RECIPROCITY

CONNECTION   TRUTH

"False happiness renders men stern and proud, and that happiness is never communicated. True happiness renders them kind and sensible, and that happiness is always shared...Success in the majority of circumstances depends on knowing how long it takes to succeed...You have to study a great deal, to know a little."

∽ Charles De Montesquieu

*H*ealth and happiness are the primary purpose of life, which is enhanced with meaningful interactions. Acquiring social interaction skills is the keystone to living a vibrant life. A relationship as defined by Merriam-Webster's dictionary as: "The way people or objects are connected or in the state of being connected; the way people or groups behave toward each other." Every country in the world has stated that social interaction is the key to achieving peace.

Personality differences influence social connections resulting in diverse types of relationships. Most assume daily chit chat is adequate for true connection; however, deeper and heart-felt connection prove to be longer lasting and more conducive to happiness for a healthy lifestyle. Interactions are most joyful with mutual and rewarding connections. Understanding personality and behavior is required for self-analysis. This, in turn, aids successful interactions.

Social interactions, together with health and attitude, can lead to a fulfilling life. If you are conscious and aware of how your behavior affects other people, you will observe how others react toward you and modify your actions. Self-awareness is key. There are several HHI books that depict the theme of interactions. This theme has many facets as demonstrated in the behaviors listed below:

1. EMOTIONS — bodily reactions (anger, sadness, joy, etc.) attributed to hormones (universally accepted), are coming from our genes and the amygdala part of the brain (root section). Thus, feelings (happiness, pleasure, etc.) are triggered by situations, personality, and beliefs whose origins (the neo-cortex) are products of the brain's emotions, which assess meaning to our emotions. Our environment affects us also.

The HHI book associated with this theme is *Belief: Integrity in Relationships* since emotions govern our belief system which helps us to decipher what we are feeling and if our conscious mind agrees with our actions. Morality is a key in most interactions and integrity is the glue that keeps us true and valid in our relationships. Becoming unique individuals helps us cope. Beliefs are opinions our minds believe.

2. CONNECTIONS — logical associations or activities with people will foster interrelated relationships. People can become intimate when engaging in social interactions. Connections are the means for verbal and non-verbal communication to take place. Body language is also key, as well as tone, and mood. We always speak the truth without words

The HHI book associated with this theme is *The Power of a Woman: Leading the Way* since connections are keys to a woman's power and behavior consequences in all types of relationships. Most successful relationships are with partners that can almost read each other's minds and have a true or clear connection in any activity in which they engage. Thus, verbal dialogue or body language is key.

3. COMPASSION — associated with sympathy and concern for the feelings of others, when understanding their situation and plight. Empathy is the ability for a person to relate to another's pain or hurt as if that person is experiencing the pain themselves. Emotional intelligence researchers state that people concerned only with their own welfare lack empathy. All relationships have some degree of intimacy.

The HHI book associated with this theme is *7 Keys to Lifelong Sexual Vitality* since the ability to sense what another person needs or is feeling is paramount in any intimate relationship. Most of us fear interactions since we try to protect ourselves from being hurt; however, unless we share who we are by expressing feelings we will lack intimacy. We are then alone.

4. ATTENTION — being focused (present) on connections being made so that daily interactions are a focal point and nothing will divert our attention. Being aware of what is

being said (shared) and listening to others intently or focusing on our own creative projects are paramount to fully realized connections. Connection occurs if attention and focus are present. Focus is the central key to attention.

The HHI book associated with this theme is *A Family's Guide to Health and Healing* since each family member needs to feel important and part of the family by being listened to and receiving adequate attention at gatherings. Eating healthy food is a family affair and must include everyone's participation. We can share who we are while enjoying healthy meals together that are fun and creative.

5. HONESTY — allowing non-verbal communication, as a key with intuitive understanding and honest connections, shows that body language cannot lie. This includes choosing appropriate healthy clothing so as not to be distracted from our greater goals. We have a misconception that what is on our skin has no correlation to our health goals; however, this is a fallacy. What we wear is very intimate and affects our well-being.

The HHI book associated with this theme is *Killer Clothes* since being healthy is the complete picture of not only what you eat, how you relate, but also what clothes you wear and how you present yourself. Your relationship to yourself includes choosing organic clothes. If your clothes are toxic, you will be also. A complete picture must be assessed for a successful healthy life.

6. INTENTION — recognizing true goals and what the inner heart wants helps us stay motivated in the quest of reaching clear and concise healthy objectives daily. This allows us to see clearly into the others' heart and soul and establishes a strong connection. Of course, self-honesty is the glue or foundation and necessary before relationship

honesty between two or more people and objects can occur.

The HHI book that is associated with this theme is *Sweet Disease*, since being completely honest about our relationship to sugar and its effects on us is a reflective mirror. Addiction to sugar, which is a health hazard, can cloud intimacy to self and others. Being transparent with who we are and what we need is revelant; being our best is only achieved by complete honesty.

Emotional Concepts

Emotions are feelings expressed as happy or sad depending on personality, mood, and coping skills. Stress is an emotional strain or tension caused by anxiety or worry, which is positive or negative. Emotions, such as anger, disgust, anxiety, worry, and depression, can lead to stressful social interactions and will produce physical, emotional, mental, or spiritual distress. Awareness of feelings can assuage these situations, as well as honest self-assessment or self-reflection. Daniel Goleman's five components, in his book, *Emotional Intelligence*, are:

1. Self-management of emotions (self-awareness)
2. Management of emotions of others (self-regulation)
3. Understanding moods of others (empathy)
4. Internal motivation of self and others (ambition)
5. Social skills and respect for self and others (social interactions).

Relationships are complex. If the above simple skills are not developed and utilized, miscommunication will occur and the real intent is lost in chaotic or unclear connections. Listening intently, with open hearts and with empathy, allows true communication. Love exists when two people think about each other with a smile, followed by happy feelings and secure thoughts. Successful interactions expand our awareness.

Mutual reciprocity is successful when we listen. Interactions are successful when we pay attention to each other's needs. People have energetic personalities that attract each other, when some people in love are asked, how do they know this is the one, they say "they just know." This is intuitive knowledge or an instinctive knowing without analytical thinking. People have friends or partners where they feel safe, loved, accepted, and respected.

Strong emotions can be creatively expressed; thus, managing feelings is fundamental to creative expression, including balancing all parts of self (especially the emotional self). A person must be confident, aware, focused, self-assured, in order to be free to express their intuitive creative self. A strong spiritual self helps center the emotional self, which helps balance emotional energy.

Multiple Intelligences

Understanding behaviors and personalities involves self-analysis. Howard Gardner was a prevalent psychologist in the later part of the last century who proclaimed we can't measure intelligence in just math and verbal ability. He produced his eight multiple intelligences theory to give us a greater understanding of the many gifts and talents that people possess. His eight intelligences are:

1. Word Smart — verbal and linguistic acuity,
2. Number Smart — math and logical ability,
3. Picture Smart — abstract thinking,
4. Body Smart — hand/eye movement,
5. Music Smart — musical talent, tone, pitch,
6. People Smart — interpersonal or social skills,
7. Self-Smart—intra-personal or self-knowledge,

8. Nature Smart—appreciating nature or outdoors.

Since we know that we are multitalented, our job is to find our gifts and share them with others. Interpersonal and intra-personal skills are predominantly emotional. They help us in relationships, as well as self-development. We only learn when we are open and accept new ideas that can change our attitude and voice. We become knowledgeable as our commitment to learn about our health and behavior is established.

Psychological theories were created to shed light on the behavior of human beings from ancient times. Ancient Greeks explained behavior via myths, dramas, and philosophies. Their theories on personality gave us insight to our own behavior. The nature versus nurture debate is always present with the answer being a combination of both, since we are a product of our environment. Our genetic composition or personality continues to evolve throughout life and adapts our personality to changes in our surroundings.

BELIEF AND HONESTY

Emotions

"It isn't enough to talk about peace. One must believe in it. And it isn't enough to believe in it. One must work at it."....."Friendship with one's self is all important because without it one cannot be friends with anyone else in the world... Yesterday is history; tomorrow is a mystery, and today is a gift. That is why we call it the present."*

✌ Eleanor Roosevelt

Belief encompasses many forms of a person's mental attitudes such as, faith, concepts, and confidence. Our emotions are important players in any type of relationship. Plutarch (a famous poet and Greek/Roman philosopher) said: "What we are about inwardly, we see and express through our emotions." We connect with ourselves, to others, or to objects via our ability to express our emotions. Our personality determines the ability to listen to our heart and feel confident. Integrity implies adherence to strict moral codes.

Since emotions have the capacity to govern our belief system, we have to be conscious of our thoughts, purpose, and actions. Belief, according to Merriam-Webster, connotes a feeling of faith or an opinion coming from our mind. Belief in love, belief in God, or belief in self, enables human beings to be confident and accomplished. Confidence is a key to success and can only be achieved through honest actions and belief in self.

Dr. Powell's value system based on her successful career in NYC financial corporations is described below:

The word "Integrity" has a broader meaning involving not only honesty, confidence, and your whole being (all parts of self), but also, honesty with a moral code. This implies honesty and sincerity for the good of the whole world, including noble behavior that can change the world.

Honesty with others can only be assured if you are honest with yourself first and able to keep promises and obligations. In ancient times your word was a contract, and bartering was the means of exchanging commodities that took the place of money and written contracts. Integrity deals with physical and emotional behavior, while belief deals with opinions and the mind. Integrity is being genuine and paying attention to what is needed, as well as authentic social interactions. Focus is the key tool to use when needing to be genuine and truthful.

Relationships can be complex in different environments,

such as work settings. We are called upon to demonstrate our gifts and talents in loving and caring relationships. It shows us the tools that we can use to participate freely without guilt, fear and worry. We need to love ourselves first before connecting with others. We are never alone; if we have a strong sense of self. You need not be insecure about being alone. You always have yourself.

Everyone searches for the perfect partner, but at times we prematurely convince ourselves this is the one. We search for true love or a soulmate to fulfill our lives; however, true love generally arrives after thirty to forty years of hard work, devotion, and compromise. Relationships and social interactions work better if there is mutual reciprocity.

The HHI book, *Belief: Integrity in Relationships,* discusses different types of relationship and how to be successful. The Belief book has three parts:

1. Part One – The Integrated Self and Sharing (relating to the parts of self, such as physical or behavior, emotional or feelings, mental or perspectives, and having belief in an honest self).

2. Part Two – Shared Selves in Balanced Relationships (relating to another requires a see-saw effect of balance so that one is fairly treated and does not feel used or taken advantage of).

3. Part Three - Our Shared Selves in the World (relating our true self to the highest level when participating and giving our gifts and talents for all to share).

A key to living with integrity is to surround yourself with honest and responsible people that you trust. Love and intimacy are virtues that come from integrity in relations. The more honest you are in expressing yourself, the more intimate you become. Intimacy is not just sexual or touching, but it also suggests connecting to another's heart, mind, soul and spirit. These types of connections, without fear, are open and straight-forward. Love is an energy flow and cannot be controlled externally. It is a feeling that is regulated by our mind and thoughts. These thoughts may change, when we feel deceived and can no longer trust.

Dr. Katherine Powell, when writing Belief, with Dr. Brian Clement, relates her experiences below:

> Truth in relationships starts with honest people who can share who they are. Belief means accepting what is true while having trust, faith, and confidence. If you don't have respect for your partner, or give with a clean heart without expectations, you develop anger and resentment. You must put your partner first and then think about others; as long as you protect yourself, when noble, you will do things with honor, ethics, and integrity.
>
> As women, we forget our boundaries and then get into difficult situations with our partner. We have responsibilities and choices to become the best we can be. Confidence is the backbone of a relationship and our health. A good example of this is Rafael Nadal, a world class tennis champion who exemplifies confidence. When he plays every move he makes is focused, purposeful, and intense. His intention is clear and piercing, which can humbly intimidate opponents; however, when the game is over, he is calm and peaceful. True internal power projects confidence and security.

Great leaders always give acknowledgment to those around them, recognizing their success. Honesty is what we strive for in ourselves and others. Without this virtue, we are only building sand castles that get washed away in high tide. The foundation of any relationship, including to ourselves or any creative endeavor, relies on the ability to be present. Heroes and people who developed virtues were not stricken by human tragic flaws. They reached their goals triumphantly by being focused and never detached.

The Belief book demonstrates that selfish, or irresponsible actions, and false pride lead to relationships that are shallow and not genuine. You cannot grow into a self-realized person reaching your full potential if you are bogged down with triviality and meaningless activities that belie your quest for greatness, joy, and fulfillment. To be fully realized is to rise out of the mire of mediocrity and reach the stars.

All the power of greatness is within you; your mind and thoughts can be self-controlled. You are present and in the zone when you stop thinking about selfish needs and let your gifts and talents rise. Be awake; know your gifts, and share them with the world. We all are in the same boat, and we can help each other reach our highest purpose. Our behavior is influenced by our attitudes, beliefs, personalities, and the value that we place on each thought and action. A compassionate self is aware of its own behavior and that of others. True connections occur with compassion and kindness.

WOMEN LEADERS

Connections

"Do what you feel in your heart to be right—for you'll be criticized anyway."... *"Great minds discuss ideas; average minds discuss events; small minds discuss people."* ... *"You must do the thing you cannot do."* .... *"A stumbling block for the pessimist is a stepping stone to the optimist."*.... *"Great leaders inspire people to have confidence in themselves."*

◢ Eleanor Roosevelt

Great accomplishments in the world were made by teams, and people working together with common goals. Leadership has been designated to men throughout history; however, as also noted, most men have had great women beside them as partners. Many of these women took over the leadership when necessary. There are many male/female partnerships in various industries that are successful as noted in this book. We can see that leadership skills include inspiring others, delegating and trusting those who surround the leader.

Dr. Katherine Powell expresses her motivation for the HHI book *The Power of a Woman*:

> Successful men have had powerful women behind them. Eleanor Roosevelt finally got women recognized in the 1940s, due to her candor and giving nature. Being the best they could be, with no fear, worked. Anger stems from fear, and even love. Be kind and give to others. Secure fatherswill always tell daughters they can do anything. Even a supportive husband can fill that role for his wife. You must have a support group or partner, family and friends, who will also play some kind of role. Men and women offer different styles, such as Ying/Yang, and must work together.
>
> In addition, leaders have to be at the helm to guide people to meet their goals. Taking care of ourselves is key. During my travels, I learned that food is what we eat when we need to get nutrients. Food is an adventure when traveling in different countries, since nutrition is dependent on the culture. Emotional eating, which occurs when we need to fill a void, can lead to addiction. We will become addicted to eating if we don't use the five senses and have a creative purpose. We know that when we share food we become connected and express our feelings.
>
> Women have been known to be in the kitchen taking care of the family, however when they have a career their outlook on food is altered. A woman's goals are broadened with families,

and she faces different challenges when she needs to provide nutrition for the family. Food is life to many cultures, but it really is the life in food that matters. In our country, women leaders are increasingly being elected in our political arena. Power can be shared between both men and women. The election of women leaders is increasing and their leadership qualities are necessary to complete complex projects.

The Merriam-Webster definition of power includes: *"The capacity or ability to direct or influence the behavior of others or the course of events."* Our history has shown we have had great female queens, generals, presidents and prime ministers, of course not in this country. We hope that America will soon follow these examples.

Leadership attributes include:

1. Honesty (trusting self and others) – keeping our word and revealing the truth strengthens our leadership qualities by being able to withstand great force, verbal storms, and debates;

2. Confidence (strength in self and others) – maintaining our self-esteem is a lifetime job that requires self-knowledge and respect to be strong and keep our acceptance of weakness at bay;

3. Organization skills (discipline) – knowing what has to be done and keeping track of goals as well as knowing the critical path is vital to achievement and communicating vital knowledge;

4. Commitment (keeping goal in sight) – keeping promises and stating the truth is an attribute that is required for great leaders, since without completion of projects, it is academic;

5. Creativity (inventive style and new ideas) – generating new ideas is required of great leaders, since there would be nothing to follow without them and guidance would be moot.

The purpose of *The Power of a Woman* was to educate and empower women with tools and inspiration to follow their dreams wit no fear. We wanted to give women guidelines for obtaining leadership qualities and to foster a healthy attitude to accomplish their goals in a tough "battleground."

Going through adversity only strengthens you, and your power is only yours and no one can take it away unless you give it away as Eleanor Roosevelt said so eloquently. She was a prime example of doing the president's job, while only being given the title of First Lady; however, she did the job and then some. During the war years of the thirties and forties, women became strong and proved how qualified they were. This was recorded in our cinematic history and lately, we have been trying to give female heroes more opportunities. Women since World War II have been steadily gaining positions in politics, corporations, and other institutions. Many men still feel threatened by women in powerful positions; however, there seems to be a growing acceptance. Hopefully, more women are believing they can succeed.

The HHI book, *The Power of a Woman,* states that authenticity and boundaries are required for great leadership. The book depicts three major sections:

1. Section One: Women and Leadership—depicting great world female leaders throughout history and their accomplishments;

2. Section Two: Balancing the Divide—describing male/female leadership qualities and differences, and how complimentary they can be;

3. Section Three: Bridging the Divide—balancing home and work has been a major goal for women; however, we can also become better male/female partners.

This book encompasses healthy guidelines for both men and

women. Readers will understand history and the battles women have endured. Personal power and greed have been more important than the betterment of the planet and our society We believe men and women can work together to better our planet, otherwise we are doomed. We are hopeful that our society will awaken and see the folly of male domination.

We can learn from examples and stories of great leadership, such as our country's Native American ancestors who had great female leaders. We know that the powers of sharing, communicating, and collaboration are the best solution to bridge the divide. It is important that women continue to be healthy and willing to be guided to do this. Men and women working together is the ideal combination for success.

We still have hope and faith that the light will dawn on our society and keep the balance of power as it should be. It was in ancient times (before 500 BC) that women had much more power and influence. Modern society has to learn from our oldest ancestors. Women could then vote, be on councils, and own property. In the 1960s, women could not own credit cards unless the husband's name was on it. In the 1970s they were browbeaten during divorce cases. We will not mention the "ME TOO" slogan now, since this reveals the outrage of sexual molestation in the workplace forever. We won't mention the male-dominated Catholic church's alleged abuse of children. Also, we will not discuss how judges considered silent or "hush" money acceptable to keep peace and power in place.

Power, through the centuries, shifted to men, who used it to manipulate the populace; however, women are progressing towards more power, but are still vulnerable to male domination. Most women, as well as men, are afraid to change the status quo since new behavior patterns must be created and the fear of change is overwhelming. The African tribes have always elected female leaders to get them through emergencies. Unfortunately, we still have to get beaten up a bit to realize the potential and power of female leadership. Men and women will benefit when they work together,

The "self" is considered to be an ego identity or the single most prominent characteristic of an individual. Understanding who you are is the primary goal for adolescence and maturation. You have to adapt to a new set of individual beliefs and values different from what you grew up with. Personality is complex, because it depends on genetics, culture, environment, and life experiences.

A centered sense of self involves alignment of the parts of self that make up an individual. As these separate selves fit together and fall into place, they become integrated. An individual can then attain the height of intellectual and creative development. Culture places a key role in defining a person and their personality. A true and unique identity develops and shapes a person into a unique individual.

We are in an emergency situation now, and unless we face the truth, we will destroy ourselves with mediocrity. Male power, sex, and greed as well as wars are games for men; however, women pay the price. Hopefully a truce will be formed in which men and women working together is normalized. When this happens everyone will prosper and be more peaceful.

PARTNERS AND INTIMACY

Compassion

"You have to accept whatever comes and the only important thing is that you meet it with courage and with the best that you have to give."....."One's philosophy is not expressed in words; it is expressed in choices one values, and the choices we make are ultimately our responsibility."...No one can make you feel inferior without your consent."

ᕫ Eleanor Roosevelt

We grew up on fairy tales; however, if we believe them to be true and real, we are open to disappointment, anger, and sadness. Men and women are continually searching for a partner to share their lives. The choices we make in life (jobs, places where we live, or partners) depend on self-knowledge and the ability to make decisions that are relevant to our personality and needs. This process is aided with truth and knowledge of what makes us happy.

A marriage is a commitment between two people who vow to be a single entity in good times, as well as, bad. In hardships, they vow to stand together as a united couple. Both partners need understanding and agreement on their type of sexual marriage to have a successful union. Merriam-Webster defines intimacy as: "Close familiarity or friendship or sexual activity between lovers." Sexual union is intimacy, whereas in olden days it could be considered courtship. This is accomplished only through honest and truthful communication.

There are different types of marriages or partnerships:

1. SEXUALLY FAITHFUL. Each individual is only having sex with his or her partner with no other sex experiences; each partner may consider their intimate coupling private and a secret.

2. SEXUAL PROMISCUITY. One partner could keep the sex vow faithfully, while the other partner has various sexual experiences; both could have secret or overt sexual experiences with others.

3. SEXUALITY NON-EXISTENT. Both partners agree that their relationship is platonic, and their friendship or partnership precludes sex; intimacy is not sexual but may be romantic or loving.

Sexual vitality implies having the type of energy exchange that satisfies both partners and can only be acceptable if communicated clearly. It is important that each person in the partnership voices their individual boundaries, without insecurities which can cause jealousies. Each person in a union needs to be clear in their intention in the relationship, what is acceptable and what isn't. Acceptance of the other's limitations is necessary for the union to work. Agreement must be procured as to the ways intimacy will be expressed for successful marriages, partnerships, or friendships. Obviously if one partner is unhappy the union will not last.

There are five basic types of marital intimate communication:

1. SEVERED – no real connection and talk is superficial, while living in delusion; each person assumes that the other is in agreement while living in their own world with no intimacy.

2. SURFACE – some superficial connection but talk is chit chat, not deep or soul satisfying; there may be mating but it is informal as a routine with no deep expression of love.

3. SHALLOW – talk is frequent but no communicating real needs or what each person is truly feeling; there is only for-

mal fornication without deep satisfaction.

4. SEPARATE – partners lead separate engaging lives and have their own interests that they share occasionally; they can be intimate with boundaries, regulated by agreeable times.

5. SATIATED – talk is real and sharing completely what each partner has experienced; there is mutually consensual intimacy where trusting feelings or emotions are reciprocated.

Some couples abuse each other by bringing their friends into disagreements in order to leverage power; however, this represents a false marriage since it depends on disrespect. Their insecurities preclude intimacy. Some couples use others as enemies to procure closeness such as, "us against them." If this works for them, then it is obviously acceptable; however, usually this union cannot last since the enemies (the victims of the couple) may revolt. Many couples experience date nights, where they go through the motions of being together; however, truly satisfying date nights include open sharing and communication with real feelings and vulnerability.

Many couples have new challenges every day, especially when they lose their partner. Couples share their ups (love, children, success) and downs (fear, loss, disappointment). Their family dynamics change, especially when the remaining partner has to continue working while keeping the family together. The process includes building a new life that strengthens the remaining partner. A new identity must be created to continue. There are many examples and Charles W. Gravener's story is included below.

Charles W. Gravener, an international top-level banking executive, worked in New York City for many prestigious financial institutions. His career enabled him to travel internationally and also allowed him to meet and grow close to many lifelong friends, including Dr. Katherine Powell, with whom he has been colleagues and friends for thirty-five years. Charles believes: "Like family, solid friends are the foundation for a happy life. These friends are the types of people that you could not speak to for a year, but when meeting again, you take up exactly where you left off. Good friends are those you can count on to be there no matter what happens."

Charles experienced many joys and tragedies in his life. Here is his story:

In 1978, I married an incredible woman who gave me three wonderful children. We decided to live where we had grown up to maintain the importance of family. Both our parents, grandparents and siblings lived nearby. This enabled our children to progress knowing support of family. For me, this meant commuting daily to Manhattan. My wife was a statistician who decided to stay home with the children, while they were in elementary school.

The children participated in community sports, such as softball, baseball, and soccer. I decided to coach their teams so that I could spend time with them. My daughter joined the Brownies and Girl Scouts, and my wife was a Den mother. My boys were both in the Cub and Boy Scouts, and I was a Den leader for both. We belonged to a church that I had attended from birth, and my children enjoyed Sunday school there. As a family, we took many summer vacations together to Disney World, Ocean City in Maryland, as well as the New Jersey shore. We both felt that it was important to spend our weekends doing something with the family in order to support and guide them.

Suddenly, tragedies started. I was in the World Trade Center on 9/11 and thankfully walked away without any injuries. The fear and events of 9/11 changed our culture from one that felt safe and secure into one that felt vulnerable. A year later we had a small fire in our home, and by the grace of God, our children were in school, and my wife was spared. A year after that, my wife collapsed with a brain aneurysm and passed away. This left our youngest in middle school; our middle child was going into college, and our oldest was a junior in college. This last tragedy created a family scar that will never be lifted.

Tragedy continued with my physical exam taken in November 2015. As a result of that physical, it was found that I had pancreatic cancer. I was fortunate that they caught it early. After an extensive operation at Jefferson Hospital in Philadelphia, I am now a five-year survivor. My medical condition keeps me very conscious of the food I eat and the maintenance of my physical and mental health. I am aware of the slogan "Let food be thy medicine" and I am choosing to embrace the opportunity to continue my healthy journey.

After surviving the operation, I decided to retire. Recently I moved to Buffalo, New York where I am able to help raise my three-year-old twin grandsons. Growing up and living in New Jersey and Pennsylvania, a move to Buffalo was quite a change in lifestyle. My mantra was always about the family, and the next venture in my life continued that mantra. I found out years ago, being a single father of three children, that I had to become self-motivated on a daily basis.

Thankfully life goes on, which is better than the alternative; however, the search for my new lifestyle is an adventure that begins with each new day, while encountering new relationships. After retirement, I joined a model Lionel train group in New Jersey. This group of thirty-five retirees meets every Wednesday morning for breakfast. About a third of these people met again at one of the houses for lunch and played with model trains for the rest of the day. This is a group of close friends who do anything and everything for each other.

Retirement also afforded me the time to volunteer at my church for preparing weekly meals for the needy. Retirement has also allowed me to join the community of senior citizens in Buffalo. Without a spouse, I find this to be a supportive group for playing cards, doing puzzles, exercising and eating, but I do not see myself fitting in. I have, however, found a group of old codgers that have taken 1940s and 1950s automobiles and restored them. These people meet weekly on summer evenings, displaying their cars while they sit around and talk about the old days when these cars were brand new. I do seem to fit into this group.

I have joined a church in Buffalo which is similar to the one from my youth, in Trenton, New Jersey. The people are very welcoming and a community of givers. My new life has begun. Once again, I cherish each day, enjoying what comes, as a blessing and a gift. My grandchildren are a great joy and this affords me the opportunity to pass on our family mantra, knowledge, love, and traditions.

Whether the single parent is male or female, the duties are similar, since he or she has to fulfill the role of the missing partner. The HHI book, *7 Keys to Lifelong Sexual Vitality*, helps couples to come to agreement and to use their sexual energy in an honest and open manner. The book is a roadmap to sexual health and to encourage sexual sharing with couples of all ages. If one has good health, sexual intimacy is desired more frequently and helps maintain vitality throughout one's lifespan. Sexual energy nourishes our minds, bodies and our spirits. Remaining sexually active is one of the most effective ways to nurture each other.

The challenges of sexual intimacy can be difficult. Attitude and nutrition are some of the techniques used to intensify sexuality. Therein are recipes rich in sex-enhancing nutrients, as well as guided mental imagery to be mindful for intimacy. There are ways to overcome sexual dysfunction and increase satisfaction. There is a need to acknowledge overcoming fear and learning to recognize any misinformation that has been communicated to increase intimacy.

Once we allow compassion for others, we can then feel our own passion. Sexual vitality thrives when we are satisfied. Many of us can shape empathy (feeling what another is feeling), which allows and enhances the magic of two people's intimacy to become potent and unforgettable. People need sharing time to get into the romantic mood for intimacy and when supported never fails. A person needs a strong sense of self before being truly compassionate with others, or else they fear losing themselves without boundaries.

The *7 Keys to Lifelong Sexual Vitality* book is divided into seven key chapters:

1. KEY ONE: Understand Your Sexuality
    Healthy sex is a potent medicine. Through our work at HHI, we have seen first-hand that people in committed relationships who maintain sexual intimacy have a three times greater chance of achieving their health recovery goals.

2. KEY TWO: Imagine Your Sexuality
    Desire starts in your mind. When developing a sane and sound vision of sexuality, your inhibitions and restrictions will change into acceptance and sharing. Redefine your view on intimacy so that your life can literally depend upon it.

3. KEY THREE: Express Your Sexuality
    Communication is both verbal and non-verbal. Most of us find it difficult to fantasize and share our fantasies with our partner, yet study after study reveals that this is healthy and helpful in keeping sexual intimacy fresh and alive.

4. KEY FOUR: Protect Your Sexuality
    Making sure you live a biologically clean life is a critical step in achieving sexual health, as well as overall health. This includes limiting your use of synthetic chemicals, junk foods, municipal water, medicines, cosmetics, personal care products, etc.

5. KEY FIVE: Nourish Your Sexuality
   Be aware of embracing and supporting your needs. Even infertility can be conquered, as we see time and time again here at Hippocrates Wellness. Most couples who are infertile resort to fertility medicine, which has a long list of side effects and few successes.

6. KEY SIX: Enhance Your Sexuality
   Channel sexual energy in your mind. Tantra grew out of this and became the first map to conscious intimacy. Learning and practicing the technique not only means controlling sexuality, but also to heighten its pleasure, stimulation and joy. Be open to new experiences.

7. KEY SEVEN: Prolong Your Sexuality
   The goal of Tantra was not necessarily to have orgasm but to prolong the heightened pleasure of sharing each other. Fantasies and sharing desires can prolong intimacy so that both partners will be satisfied.

Sexual energy is a universal fuel of life, such as nourishing the human mind, body, and spirit, with diet and exercise. The body, and mind (your thoughts), all work together to prolong sexual vitality. Spirited awakening through sexual intimacy has been practiced since ancient times in India and China. Books, such as the *Kama Sutra*, were known to the world as important practices for good health. Healthy sex is a potent medicine and people taking pills for depression and anger could often discard them with a loving sexual lifestyle. There is no age limit to great sex. Intercourse is wonderful, but as we get older, we many have to adjust our expression, since hormones affect our desire and performance.

Some love to be touched, like massaging before sexual intimacy occurs, which should satisfy both partners, whether giving or receiving (cuddling). Intimacy in relationships is easy if real communication takes place and there are no personality disorders such as, narcissism.

When one or both partners are selfish and cannot give of themselves, it usually means there is no true sense of self to give; therefore, the intimacy is not real or only one partner may be satisfied. The goal is to have two people share in an intimate act giving much of who they really are. When it is real (no delusion) or playful fantasy, it is very powerful and the energy will never die or dissipate.

HOME REMEDIES

Attention

"Human behavior flows from these main sources: desire, emotions, and knowledge.... The truth is rarely pure and never simple.... Let us be grateful for the mirror in revealing to us our appearance only..... The great gift of human beings is that we have the power of empathy."
                                          ↝ *Plato*

Family dynamics can be complicated, and many families are considered dysfunctional; however, people are becoming aware of their poor communication skills and lack of family interactions. Honest sharing by eating together and caring for each other's health can help family dynamics. Merriam-Webster defines dysfunctional as: "Deviating from the norms of social behavior in a way regarded as bad; not operating normally or properly." In our new age of super electronics, most families don't sit together for meals or if they do, they are on cell phones, texting or playing their games on computers. We as a society are aware of this phenomenon and we need a family's guide with healthy ideas to solve this disruptive concern.

It is important to care for each other and share part of the day as a family unit through group activities, games, or movies. Keep family interaction alive. Eating healthily and preparing meals or shopping for home remedies can assist in building self-esteem and self-respect. When children become involved, they sense they are being cared for and loved. The HHI book, *A Families' Guide to Health and Healing*, helps when families create activities that connect them, such as in gatherings fostering belonging and loved feelings. Everyone should participate.

Family gatherings are a great responsibility and parents cannot be inebriated, since that precludes genuine interaction. In fact, this is an example for children to behave likewise and creates an empty vacuum showing that they are not cared for or truly loved. A family is a group of people (related by blood, marriage or friendship) who belong together and interact in a variety of activities, as well as being cared for (shelter, food, clothes). We learn about behavior from our families.

As Kurt Lewin (first American sociologist) said: Behavior is a product of one's personality and the environment; therefore, parents and guardians have the job of providing the proper environment for the health of their children.

Below are five aspects of developing a safe home:

1. CARING – displaying kindness and concern for others, as well as being sympathetic and understanding, fosters a healthy environment; being good-natured is vital for safety.
2. CUISINE – sharing recipes and being in the kitchen together is a loving activity that all human beings enjoy; food prep with love is felt by all.
3. COMMITMENT – being in a family means that you are there for the long haul and you are responsible for the welfare of those around you, as well as yourself.

4. COMMUNICATION – sharing yourself through verbal or nonverbal expressions is required for a family to feel connected and cared for, or else it is a house and not a home.

5. CONVIVIALITY – being friendly, warm, with an abundance of social and joyful activities, increase family togetherness which is the foremost goal of every functional family.

Creating a safe and loving environment is critical. Getting involved in community activities (church, or social clubs, etc.) is vital for developing a strong sense of self with healthy boundaries and authentic character. You can hide from yourself but not from others. We need genuine interactions to feel strong and present. This responsibility falls on every home with parental guidance. Children's identity (who they are) and their strong sense of self, develops when living in a convivial and loving home. Family harmony grows as loving and caring interaction increases.

The fourteen chapters of the HHI book, *A Families Guide to Health and Healing*, include the following concepts:

- CHAPTER ONE: A Brief History of Traditional Medicine

Alternative medicine modalities such as acupuncture are currently more acceptable in western tradition. There is a new bridge being created between alternative and western medicine. Modern world is a global village, and we can share healing traditions from every part of the globe.

- CHAPTER TWO: Hydration: You Need Pure Liquids

We should drink half of our body weight in ounces to keep our bodies hydrated daily. We should drink water at least two hours before meals, but not during meals. Additionally we should drink water at least twenty minutes after eating. Approximately 70 percent of our bodies are water. The best sources of water are steamed-distilled and highly refined filtration.

- CHAPTER THREE:
  Raw Living Herbs and Grasses in Healing

  Grass contains vital elements that complete most of our nutrition needs. Blue-green algae is also equivalent and even more complete for nutritional value. We can use herbs from nature such as Valerian, a sedative for nerves, as well as Kava-Kava for stress and depression. The herb of wild indigo is also helpful for cold sores and herpes.

- CHAPTER FOUR: Nutritional and Topical Use of Living Herb and Edible Weeds

  In ancient times, dandelion weeds and parsley were considered an important diuretic. Eucalyptus leaf is also a solution for asthma. Raw mint leaves comfort diarrhea and dried ginger powder helps relieve fever. Milk thistle helps the liver.

- CHAPTER FIVE: Baths, Thermal and Oxygen Therapies and Garlic: Nature's Powerhouse

  Oxygen is needed in the blood to feed the lungs and other organs. Honeysuckle is used for pessimism and despair. Rock Rose can be employed for anxiety, fear and panic. Sweet Chestnut can be used for anguish and fear. Things such as toiletries (soap, toothpaste, commercial deodorants), can be toxic and irritating to our skin and weaken our immune systems. Use only pure choices.

- CHAPTER SIX: Essential Oils: Aromatherapy

  Oils help alleviate physical and emotional tension. Black Pepper for cataracts, camphor for acne and bruises, fennel for alcoholism, hyssop for deep calm breathing, hormonal balance and dermatitis.

Ginger can be used for confidence and emotional strength, and orega-no for enthusiasm, intensity and vigor.

- CHAPTER SEVEN: Solutions for Common Problems

Herbs are always available. Chamomile is used for sleep; organic sulfur, kelp, nettle leaf and willow bark, are all remedies for arthritis. Vitamin E, calcium, magnesium and selenium can all be used to alleviate hypertension. Echinacea, goldenseal, summa nitrate and cat's claw support the immune system.

- CHAPTER EIGHT: Our Clothing & Our Environment: What is on Us & Around Us

We should be aware of our surroundings, as they can affect our health in ways that we cannot imagine. Organically grown and natural clothings are important for the health of our families. Our skin is our largest organ, and absorbs toxicity rapidly. We need to be aware that even seemingly harmless lotions are often toxic.

- CHAPTER NINE: Baths, Thermal, and Oxygen Therapies

Epsom salt has been commonly used in baths for relaxation and calming our nerves. Bathing can also be a healing activity, since our skin absorbs the soothing effects of the water. Clove oil baths, baking soda baths, ginger baths and lavender baths can all be used. Hyperbaric oxygen therapy is a modern method of using oxygen to improve one's health.

- CHAPTER TEN: Body Therapies and Massage

HHI has an incredible massage team that is gifted in rendering therapeutic body work for long-term benefits. There are many varieties of therapies such as shiatsu, craniosacral, deep tissue and lymphatic drainage, which all protect the body from infection and improve the functioning of the internal organs and immunity.

- CHAPTER ELEVEN: Acupuncture without needles

The specialized technique of acupuncture can help release anxiety and balance physical systems. Zone therapy and reflexology are major traditional health techniques throughout the world. Use the pressure points throughout the body such as, the feet, the ears, and the hands. Trust yourself for healing and wellness.

- CHAPTER TWELVE: Electronic and Magnetic Therapy

Our bodies are made of electrons that flow. We consist of energy and vibration. Magnetic therapies strengthen the electrical highway system of the body. We can also use electromagnetic therapy and frequency therapy clinically to assist remedies for serious conditions.

- CHAPTER THIRTEEN: Things Look Better When You See Better: Improve Vision

Check eyes periodically. The importance of sight is obvious; for example, we say, "I see" rather than "I understand." To nourish our minds and bodies we can use aloe vera, gingko biloba and zinc. To nourish our eyes, specifically, employ food-based Vitamin C, Vitamin A, and E. Wheatgrass juice is also helpful.

- CHAPTER FOURTEEN: Conclusion

Health really starts at home. The care of self and our environment promotes a healthy life. Responsibility is rewarding. As we care for ourselves, our immediate and extended families and our environment, we make the world better. When we say "Hearth and Home" we mean that the heart is in the home.

Mealtimes are an important opportunity for families to be together, to express their feelings and experiences. We all require a feeling of belonging and comfort. The best way to enjoy family gatherings is to provide a variety of tasty salads, dressings for the sprouts, inventive recipes from seeds and nuts and foods that can be steamed or require limited heat. This enables friends and family to enjoy and share meals, and have been a mainstay for families around the world for eons. The comfort of being together is of utmost importance and being allowed to be who you are with certain rules of behavior for table etiquette is important. Families who share stay together.

CLOTHES AND SAFETY

Honesty

"Every heart sings a song, incomplete, until another heart whispers back.....A human being needs to recognize and strive to live in accordance with 'The Truth' which is embedded in realism.... You can discover more about a person in an hour of play than a year of conversation... Living a healthy life involves knowing who you are, your needs, and your personal environment."

ఴ Plato

Truth is valuable when health and happiness are concerned. Without honest self-evaluation, the path to wellness will be difficult. Our responsibility to be healthy includes clothing that we wear and avoiding all toxins. Being transparent with all our activities will affirm our health and happiness. Ancient wisdom valued being honest and working with the best of you to share with others. In ancient Greece, environment and personal hygiene played an important part in well-being. Part of the process at Delphi was bathing before worship, and above the bath basin was a sign that read "Know Thyself." In addition, Plato wrote about living with four virtues to guide us:

1. Wisdom – Knowledge and experience of yourself
2. Temperance – Be careful not to overindulge
3. Courage – Keep moving forward avoiding obstacles
4. Justice – Doing what's right and fair with judicious reasoning

These moral guidelines were commendable character traits. The ancients regarded these achievements as excellent objectives. The Greeks knew the secrets to health, relationships, and happiness. In those days, things were very simple, and life followed fundamental health rules. "Let food be thy medicine," said Hippocrates. We are still listening to those very words today and they are the cornerstone of the HHI lifestyle. We can learn from the ancients.

Our health is affected by everything around us, including our homes and workplaces. What we are exposed to on a daily basis and how we interact in our daily lives affects our health. We have to be real about our surroundings and what we put on our bodies since our skin takes in toxic material. Proper food, clothing, shelter, and restful sleep are the most significant aspects of a long and healthy existence. The HHI book, *Killer Clothes*, teaches us.

We must be aware of the atmosphere around us, such as the air we breathe, air conditioners, allergens that may invade our environment, and also heed warnings about lotions and toxic creams. We must be educated enough to recognize toxic influences, such as metal in our teeth, or fabric made of chemicals. We need courage to act with conviction, since without determination and commitment we are at the mercy of our environment.

Dr. Anna Maria, HHI co-founder, relates her views on organic clothing:

We at Hippocrates are opening the door further so you can make informed choices about the clothes you wear. Made out of the finest organic and natural fabrics, sustainable apparel nurtures the environment and contributes to the greater health of those who live consciously. Eco-friendly and irritation-free garments are free of chemicals, heavy metals, bleach, and We at Hippocrates are opening the door further so you can make informed choices about the clothes you wear. Made out of the finest organic and natural fabrics, our sustainable apparel nurtures the environment and contributes to the greater health of those who live consciously. Our eco-friendly, irritation-free garments are also free of chemicals, heavy metals, bleach, and harmful dyes. These garments are as pure and soft as possible.

Sexy intimates are specially designed to use minimal to no elastic. Any elastic in garments is fully covered with natural fabric to protect those who have sensitivities. Those who have skin allergies know that what you put on your body is as important as what you put in your body; as our skin is the largest organ, it absorbs over 60 percent of whatever comes close to it. The breathability of natural fabric is far superior to synthetic fabric, such as polyester or nylon (which is currently used in most garments on the market). It is especially critical to wear undergarments of organic fabrics, since polyester suffocates the skin. Many organic fabrics also provide the benefit of being naturally anti-bacterial and anti-fungal, which is an added plus for dermatological and gynecological health. As we develop a sense of style while we are defining ourselves, we can pick clothing that is reflective of our personalities and still be natural and comfortable. Our sense of well-being is affected by what we wear and our immediate environment.

In addition to nurturing the skin, we make sure that we are protecting the environment and have a minimal carbon footprint. Organic intimates and other garments are made using the finest sustainably sourced organic and natural fibers. We should give ourselves the gift of health; be sexy and congruent by wearing organic for our well-being.

Our awareness must also extend to the buildings we work in, the transportation we use, and the mattresses and sheets on which we sleep. Cotton and natural products are our best allies in this war of the chemical invasion that surrounds our every move. We can help our own environment and be conscious of where we go and what we use. Our health and welfare are dependent on our ability to know the truth about what we are using or abusing and it's time to take a stand and fight for our health and emotional wellness. Wellness is a responsibility. We need to be aware of our mindset and emotional condition.

Three attributes help us to stay aware of our surroundings:

1. CONSCIOUSNESS — we need to be awake and open to what and where we are, as well as what we are doing in our daily lives. Since without being aware we are puppets to the decisions others have made for us.

2. COURAGE — we need not be afraid of being different or facing judgment since we understand the harm these unnatural and unkind events can bring. Thus we are responsible for our own safety and health within our power to be brave.

3. KNOWLEDGE — we need to learn how products affect us so that we will make choices and wise decisions that put our health and well-being first. We must not be victims of established decisions beyond our control.

We need to intentionally become aware of our environment

and the people we choose to associate with, as well as where we spend time such as, work, worship, and clubs. Our will, intention, and awareness keeps us healthy. As Kurt Lewin said, "Our behavior is the product of our personality and our environment." It is our responsibility to keep ourselves safe by "keeping our eyes open,"

The HHI book, *Killer Clothes,* brings our attention to the importance of our environment, and that the chemicals we ingest, put on our bodies, or breathe can be toxic. We need to be determined and conscious of our living habits. Our intention is good health. Every move we make to increase awareness will help our journey.

There are five aspects that help us keep our personal environment healthy:

1. Music — We can be calm and hear our inner voice when we are relaxed. Music helps us ease stress in our lives. Listening can help us focus.

2. Friends — A good support system, including friends and family that sincerely care about our welfare, makes us aware and accountable.

3. Hobbies — We need to place our attention on activities that are healthy to keep us on our path. Our homes require healthy interests, movements, and family events.

4. Exercise — We need to keep moving under all circumstances. Swimming is the best, however walking or any activity that helps us remain mobile and healthy is good.

5. Support — We can help our environment by volunteering to clean parks, oceans, and beaches. Our awareness and things we do will influence others to act the same.

We need to be wise and aware of all of our choices to avoid unhealthy bodily reactions. Our wellness task includes reading and learning about toxins. This involves knowing what we select to ingest, what products we use for our skin as well as the air we breathe. Our well-being is top priority.

HEALTH WITHOUT SUGAR

Intention

"The future belongs to those who believe in the beauty of their dreams."…. "With the new day comes new strength and new thoughts."…. "The purpose of life is to live it, to taste experiences to the utmost, to reach out eagerly and without fear for newer and richer experiences."

✍️ *Eleanor Roosevelt*

We are human beings on a planet that worships sugar, especially in the last two hundred years. The manufacture of sugar from sugar cane has cost many lives from disease and hurt the slaves who were stolen from their original birthplaces to harvest it. We have placed a premium on sugar which is now killing us. We need to emotionally, mentally and physically detox, and be fully aware of the harm that sugar creates in our lives and well-being. We must understand sinister history.

Sucrose is a table sugar that should be avoided altogether; however, the main sugar problem is glucose and fructose ingested from fruits, vegetables and complex carbs, which all become the same in the small intestines. We are aware of recent studies (British journal) stating that the brain needs sugar since it does not store it. If we want alertness, increased attention span, and improved concentration food-derived sugar helps; however, in moderation. This is our challenge and lesson in life. Two much sugar creates havoc and disease. As Plato said: "Temperance is a virtue." The HHI book, *Sweet Disease*, educates us.

We know the brain needs glucose and does not store it so daily amounts of a little sugar from vegetables are important for clarity and brain power. However, the problem with sugar is its type and how much we ingest. The crisis is when it is overdone. Studies show that healthy people can eat small amounts of fruit (not to exceed 25mg) and people with blood sugar challenges have to avoid it altogether.

Dorothy Lake, a New York executive, after facing devastating news of the loss of her loved ones, realized it took a toll on her. In 2006, she started to experience pain in her joints and excruciating back issues. She conditioned herself to forge forward no matter what. Dorothy felt it was her duty not to complain. She finally made the following decisions:

I immediately cut out sugar, processed foods, alcohol, refined products, breads and pastas, dairy and all animal products. I began to get better. The results were consistent and steady. As a true educated New Yorker, I needed more. I went back to school to study raw food culinary prep as well as integrative holistic nutrition and ayurvedic principles. As I lived this new lifestyle, my life improved one hundred fold. I was able to not only be free of all pharmaceutical drugs, but also dance and sing and have free movement and truly LIVE joyously, happily and healthfully.

I lived for three months in residency learning from the masters of this protocol and soon thereafter opened the first ever Raw Vegan Juice Bar and Organic Café in the Hamptons (New York) where I preached this protocol and served foods and juices that aligned with this way of self-healing. It was so successful, people came from far and wide to speak with me about their ailments and to see if this protocol would work with them. I freely shouted from the mountain top, sharing my story with anyone who was serious in taking full responsibility for their health and life. They had to do the work it takes to free themselves from the shackles of convention, and also be open enough to see how easy it could be to be free of pain and suffering at their own hands and by their own choices. It is that simple. Do you choose to live or die? I choose to live and live joyously and freely.

Our metabolic syndrome caused by high carbs has skyrocketed obesity to the highest point in history. Fructose, sucrose and glucose are all forms of sugar, as well as any grains or potatoes. We love our carbs and they symbolize our world's comfort foods; therefore, we must find another means for comfort. The beverage and soda companies have made trillions of dollars on selling us their inexpensive sugar drinks that we have become addicted to; therefore, it is naturally difficult to stop. We have become victims; therefore we have to be honest with ourselves and our behavior. Honesty is required to reverse bad habits, as well as the will and commitment to endure.

There are five important considerations when ingesting sugars:

1. Balance, the food you eat. If you ingest sugar, make sure it is balanced with plant protein, so it is not extreme which causes blood sugar spikes. Energy is constantly flowing when you have a balanced approach to eating, as well as alertness.

2. Meditation or Qigong, brings attention to overeating via self-awareness to food habits, and the mind/body connections are also revealing actions. Meditation calms. Music, color, and guided meditation help limit sugar ingestion.

3. Addiction is common to human beings. We are sugar addicts and our "go to" food sources are inundated with high fructose corn syrup, and other hidden sugars. We want more of what feels good. Our habits are difficult to change; therefore, we have to first reveal them.

4. Depression is a by-product of sugar indulgence, since after producing much energy, you get fatigued rapidly. Sugar causes depression (highs and lows), hinders heart health, AIDS, cancer, diabetes and obesity, the number one disease.

5. Limitation of carbs and sugars helps avoid using sugar as a comfort food. Sugar intake should be minimal, if ever. Avoid trans-fats like the plague; limit rice, pasta, and bread, and other taste-good choices. The only true answer is to develop a healthy plan.

Sugar affects our personality, as well as, our behavior. We get a sugar high that promotes rapid energy but then quickly depresses us; therefore; logically, the benefit of processed sugar is nil. Research has proven more diseases are caused by sugar consumption then can be enumerated. We need to accept the fact that our sugar fantasies have gone awry and it is time to substitute our go-to comfort food with other activities that prolong our health and our life.

Dr. Katherine Powell relates an A-hah! moment during her 2014 trip to Rome, Italy when she realized that sugar was not the reward, but that feeling connected was. Her realization was manifested during her visit to LARYS Restaurant in Rome. Katherine relates her experience below:

True nourishment comes from the heart. If authentic, food goes straight to our soul; thus, you are not hungry when you are fed properly with nourishment, since you feel like you belong. I learned from HHI how important juicing was (cucumber, celery, pea, and sunflower sprouts) which only adds to the many shades of green that benefit us. Sprouts come in all shades of green, and we must appreciate their advantage. Green was always my favorite color, but now I realize why. Green food is the staff of life, and is the only true comfort food.

When eating using the five senses, such as listening to music, feeling or touching textures, tasting magnificent flavors, seeing their array of colors, and sensing aromas that dazzle, you will become gratified, satisfied, and happy. When all these senses come together it's like an explosion of joy, and you feel complete and satiated. Thus, in early December, when, for the first time, I walked into LARYS , a serene restaurant decorated in white with a red divan, I felt safe and secure. I was home.

I realized, at that moment, that I was with a loving family who were granting my every wish, giving me delicate food with special freshness and a presentation that welcomed me. The salad was full of surprises. The vegetables sang in unison with the rice and other great dishes. I was in love with artichokes. Food usually was something that did not satisfy me, because it was never authentic. Healthy and nutritious food feeds your body, mind and spirit with love. You get a purposeful soul depicting your real self. You are your best with great nourishing food. When satisfied, there is no addiction; there is no emptiness or black hole of sorrow. The result is a feeling of love, acceptance, and satisfaction.

Our soul, buried within our personality, causes us to become like zombies looking for our next sugar rush. Research has shown that the addictive brain activity is the same for opioids as for sugar. We cannot afford to jeopardize our health on such a harmful and fleeting commodity. As we gain wisdom, we are more aware of the consequences so let's put our knowledge into action. We can overcome any addiction by choosing correct foods to nourish us and by being aware of our feelings. The HHI book, *Sweet Disease*, helps us understand our sugar relationship.

Our emotional selves will thrive without sugar, even though we have doubts. The stronger we become in our core sense of self, by increasing our self-respect, and self-confidence, we will accept our lives without sugar. Unfortunately, sugar is hidden in many "foods" and even reading labels could be deceptive; thus, the safest avenue is to eat local market, fresh vegetables, and sprouts. Organic is important, but growing our own vegetables is, of course, ideal. The impact of food becomes clear when we change our reality.

We understand how harmful sugar can be, and we need to be diligent, on a daily basis. We can't fall into the trap of thinking that it is OK to eat sugar to briefly feel great. This builds up when we forget that we consistently make bad choices. We continue to make these bad choices, saying "Well it is already done;" however, the delusion fools us and eventually we will really harm ourselves. We have to be honest and real.

Our relationship to sugar is simply addicting and is interconnected with the following:

1. INTIMACY – we use sugar to fill a black hole of loneliness or sadness and crave connection

2. TASTE – we love the feeling of it in our mouths exciting our taste buds and then crave it as we give in

3. AVAILABLE – we can always grab some from anywhere via vending machines or junk food vendors and "health stores"

4. CULTURE – we see it, hear it, and are overwhelmed with its presence even if we don't want it.

5. ENERGY – we feel it as it synthetically boosts us when we are low and want that high feeling.

Basic emotions, joy, anger, sadness, fear, etc. are changing constantly, and our mind chooses, (from the neocortex part of our brain), how we feel and ways to express it. We change our emotions through affirmative thoughts. If we decide to be happy, then we will think positive thoughts. Our attitudes trigger emotions depending on situations, our opinion, and personality.

We know that the world will not get rid of sugary drinks, even with concrete evidence that they are harmful. We know this battle is on for the foreseeable future; however, there are inroads and changes on the horizon. The current trend in our culture is to eat less meat and sugar. Perhaps this will someday be a comprehensive reality. We know obesity is on the, rise and we need to start a campaign for "life without sugar". We will do this with awareness and courage, as well as education and practice.

INTUITIVE INTERACTIONS

Additional Stories

We build awareness and self-trust when we use our intuition. A confident person has integrated a strong sense of self. Self-confidence implies a deep belief in the authentic you and is derived from Latin which means "trust within self." When we build self-awareness and self-trust, we can use intuition to make healthy choices. Self-esteem, which is literally self-perception, and self-concept, are the means where you recognize your persona and self-confidence. Confidence is key for sustaining goals.

Confidence is maintained through a personal formula of knowledge that builds upon a balanced sense of self. When emotions are not in harmony, it is difficult to express oneself. Emotional stability and centering aid in enhancing self-worth. Old messages of self-doubt can hinder your expression. Feeling confident through practice can overcome fear.

Our esteemed colleague Dr. Catherine Boyle, Ph.D. in Psychology and Counselor of Education, has overcome physical and emotional challenges, such as multiple sclerosis, a debilitating neurological disease. Devoting herself to perpetual exercise and a plant-based nourishing cuisine, she abolished what physicians called "incurable disease." Not only did she rewrite her life script, but she manages a fitness center as well.

Dr. Boyle's support system consisted of her son, her ex-spouse who remained her best friend, and an assortment of co-workers and friends. She recognized the fear that they all had in learning of her disorder. Not one of them predicted a positive outcome from such a devastating prognosis. Part of her ability to supersede the naysayers was to raise the consciousness of her supporters. Immersing herself in this noble campaign to squash her malady gave her the courage, strength, and perseverance to succeed. Here is Dr. Boyle's story:

I married my high school sweetheart after nine years of dating, and I loved my life and family. My greatest gift from God was our son. He arrived with kidney disease and had numerous operations between birth and seven years of age. He now is a fine healthy young man, a high school teacher and soon to be married. Sadly, I separated from my husband after 13 years of marriage. It's been 21 years but we are still very good friends and always will be. My son came first and we never wanted him to suffer at the hands of a label, child of divorce, or split home. As a matter of fact, his elementary school teachers were unaware of our situation. We were very involved in his education and we both were on the PTA board. This filled my void of missing my counseling profession. My ex-spouse used his expertise in construction and painting to build playgrounds and sets for the school plays. He is a great father and still our biggest support. As a matter of fact he is my Health Care Proxy.

I tell you all of this as it speaks directly to the importance of relationships, both personally and professionally. Healthy relationships are directly related to wellness. Unhealthy relationships are directly related to sickness. It's black and white. No gray. God first and foremost has always been by my side, walked with me, listened to my pleas and cries for help and provided healing as well as guidance. God knows all I've endured and my experiences. This is my spiritual nourishment. While I have many friends, my closest friends list is small, maybe ten – a confidant group, if you will. These people come from high school and college. I also have made several friends over the latter years in my professional arena.

At 40, I had an "autoimmune disease" that rocked my world and forced me to take a look at my life and slow down. I was fearful as I was told I would be in a wheel chair in two years and decided to take a year off from my counseling position to get my life under control. This was devastating as I had always defined myself by my career.

Overworked, stressed, overweight and tired are the makings of a formidable disorder. I found a fitness center that worked with people who had MS and hit the ground running. I met women in wheelchairs who encouraged me to exercise regularly, something that the doctors discouraged and I was unhealthy and obese. I worked with a trainer two to three times a week and participated in classes, lacing it with my own cardio. I never lost one pound during five years. I was eating well Monday through Friday, but weekends were a free for all. I never bothered to look at calories in or calories out. Again my goal was to stay out of the wheelchair.

Being Italian was not conducive to my health. I did, however, get a job at the gym two nights a week and alternate weekends to give my former spouse time with our son. The job turned full time and I began my weight loss journey. In 2006 we created the biggest loser at the gym. I lost 110 pounds in 10 months and then 100 pounds more along the way. According to my neurologist, exercise was the single biggest element of my success.

He could only explain how exercise kept me on my feet while MRIs showed someone who should be in wheelchair. I went on to meet with specialists who agreed.

I am comfortable in my own skin and love to relax with my aromatherapy, especially clover scents. I meditate and have an attitude of gratitude upon rising and retiring daily. I list five things that make me grateful. I try to be strong and even though I face hardships and uncertainties just as many people do, there's a way forward bringing a brighter day ahead. I try not to let the crazy difficult days get me down and put things in perspective, to laugh when I can and cry when I must. I try to be everything to my family and friends and an inspiration to others. My interpersonal relationships have also been the source of healing. They can be negative if we let them. The point is that love and relationships make all the difference. True friends are the friends who will ride the bus with you when the limo breaks down and are those who share your joys and sorrows. They are by your side for the long haul, wanting you to be happy even when you are not part of their happiness. Friends have to let each other be who they are and accept each other unconditionally.

Know your values and connect with those who share them and support you. If they are selfish and only concerned with themselves they will take away your energy. Stay away from too much negativity, which only results in making you emotional. Remember you know what you need. You have to balance your physical, emotional, and mental selves to have a chance at happiness (physical well-being). Emotional joy and spiritual bliss come when you realize you are not a victim. If overwhelmed with emotions, you can easily fall prey to emotional vampires. You are the master of your own fate and everyday life.

When Catherine attended the Hippocrates Health Institute program, she lost an additional 30 pounds. She elevated her understanding of self-healing and is now a passionate propagator of the HHI lifestyle. Dr. Boyle's emotional health amalgamated to empower her heart with the abundance of empathy required to conquer past demons. She continues on her journey.

Brian relates his romantic initial meeting with Anna Maria, in Sweden:

April of 1978 was a pinnacle moment in my life. Strapped into the airplane seat next to Ann Wigmore, the founder of Hippocrates Health Institute, we landed in Stockholm, Sweden. We were soon whisked up and driven to the heart of the city where we were presenting a three- day conference. Uniquely, the weather was sunny and warm, uncommon to Scandinavia in early spring. As we climbed up the stairs to the eloquent facility, which housed a conference hall and luxurious vegan restaurant, my eye caught a smiling, long- haired woman. My heart skipped a beat. As the days passed, and hours mounted, it was difficult for me not to glance at her glowing persona. At the finish of the conference on Sunday evening, I rendered enough courage to meet her and within a minute had fallen in love. This was well over four decades ago and every day my commitment and love grows.

Anna Maria was directing Sweden's and Europe's most renowned center for inflammatory disorders. What struck me was how similar our work was on different continents. As we spoke, the similarities accumulated and I started to recognize that somehow the universe had put us together. In 1980, my future wife, Anna Maria, resigned the directorship and came to work with us at Hippocrates, which was then located in the heart of Boston. To me, it was remarkable that someone from a faraway land, speaking a different language, had the courage and foresight to make the leap. She herself brought to the Institute the long-standing tradition of the European natural health care system.

Together, we forged the foundation of what the Institute is today from the primal system that Ann Wigmore had envisioned. Together, in 1987, we pulled our roots up from the dismal winters of New England and moved the Center to sundrenched South Florida. Slowly we gathered a team of gifted and passionate professionals. All of us together expanded our offerings and increased the possibilities for people to heal themselves.

Becoming apparent was the seeming universal lack of happiness. Person after person discussed sorrowful events that often manifested into disease. We all aspire for those who attended to release their body and mind burdens so that they once again are able to refill their lives with extraordinary endeavors. What is nice, as co-directors, Anna and I help to smooth the rough edges in each other so that the encounters we have with others can be more effective and positive. We continue to develop together.

HHI has been life changing for many people, each having their own story with various levels of health issues. Each person has been motivated to educate themselves in the latest health modalities. HHI fosters individual client support and education in every guest's pursuit of healing. Since all experiences are based on health, education, and background, each guest has their own unique perspective.

Needless to say, it is essential for us to stop searching for happiness from others. We are islands unto ourselves that require care and maintenance. The most important engine behind our requirements is that of self-generated joy. When projecting this contagious emotion, it naturally attracts like-minded people who will further enhance your blossoming happiness. Avoid the entrapment of conformity by refusing to plummet into the gutter and think and speak negatively. Even when it is difficult for you to project affirmative words and thoughts, practice by doing so anyway. You will disarm your own discord by relying on your higher self.

A recent HHI guest has been writing in his journal about his marriages and several relationships. Below is his experience.

Relationships need constant vigilance. Now at seventy I learned that nothing needs more nurturing than our intimate relationship. I still learn the hard way with a recent breakup. I have pages of emails Abby wrote to me explaining why she was done, I have saved and or printed them out to review in detail. Much was miscommunication, not being on the same page, and instead of asking for clarity or having an in-depth discussion it got swept under the rug. We are both great people, lots of zest for life and possibility. We still couldn't pull off keeping it together while working through our issues. We are people pleasers and avoid arguing or raising our voices. Neither one of us were able to throw a flag or call a timeout. It was just easier to keep quiet.

We had great chemistry overall. We could talk about most anything (except our issues). We enjoyed staying fit, doing simple social activities, walking, some biking, movies, dinner, family events, and some day trips and a couple of weekend trips. We laughed easily and just felt good together. Through manyperiod it was pajama night most weekends. Abby stayed at her daughter's condo and the office when she could not work at home. Then Abby was informed her first ex-husband wanted to come up from Florida to stay with his daughter (with whom he had a distant relationship. Tom was described as a grumpy, rich, old man who booted Abby from her bedroom on weekends. Since I had not made my condo comfortable for her, she was relegated to family and traveling to see girlfriends. She had perhaps a mild nervous breakdown, and our relationship finally cracked, and ended over the next couple of months.

We started communicating after Abby was committed to splitting up. We emailed about all the things that bothered us and things we should have been talking about all along. Most everything Abby brought up was important to her such as ignoring or dismissing her issues and not taking any action or explaining why there was no action taken. I usually made a compromise or low budget option. Looking back, here are some lessons learned or at least to be explored:

1. Abby chose me, which is a recommended method for getting involved to begin with, to have the woman choose the man. We had our first date at a local restaurant and both walked away with doubt and internal dialog. While driving I decided to text her and share my internal dialog. And she did the same. I told her I felt I couldn't afford her. She was dressed up, with a lot of jewelry and just appeared to be an upper class woman that liked the finer things in life. Her internal dialog was something like "He doesn't like me."

2. It probably took a couple of months of dating, getting to know one another and surmounting a few hurdles in this season of life. We started picking up momentum and attending each other's church, meeting family, and spending all of our extra time together.

3. It usually doesn't take too long for little things to start popping up. A comment here or there, or behaviors in and around the house that push buttons. Down the road bigger issues surface like level of commitment, living together or marriage, or how money is spent and on what? Depending on the personalities of the couple and their level of communication, this is where some of the difficult times begin.

In our case, living arrangements were an issue, as well as money. Also, differences in the way I languaged my metaphysical spirituality became a problem to where Abby didn't want me to go to church with her. Numerous little things according to Abby and her emails included: the sleigh Amish sofa I didn't buy her, and not preparing more in the condo to make it comfortable for her. We were overwhelmed with problems.

As all of these things, little and not so little, cropped up over the years. Instead of getting them out on the table for discussion, work life, and other stressors took precedence. My communication patterns were different from Abby's and I didn't make the move to be sure we discussed things. There were times that Abby stewed over things and I wouldn't know about it. Since I was not aware, our situation developd into layers of problems.

Each of us is filled with abundant, loving power that is meant to be your personal imprint on the world within which you live. From the second that you come into existence at conception, your being is engaged in perpetual forward movement. There are no pauses, only a continuum of activity, events, and environments. It is how you perceive and process this activity that molds you into an optimist or a pessimist. All positive processes require acceptance of greatness in even the events that appear stressful. The stress is brought upon ourselves from the lack of commitment we make in finding the loving message that is always wrapped somewhere within the occurrence. As we march forward, and the days and years pass, affirmative outcomes gather together to create a life of passionate pursuits and memories of happiness. We learn from every experience.

The mission at HHI is to help everyone achieve their health goals and to continue down the road of happiness. Below are the seven key practices for a healthy and happy life:

The 7 Keys to Discovering YOU in You

1. ACCEPTANCE: This poignant word generally renders an image of you agreeing with something that you really don't agree with. Now it is time to re-think it. What we must accept, or better yet, whom we must accept is ourselves. Every aspect of what makes us complete has to be built upon high integrity. Whatever endeavor, idea, persona, or thought we contemplate and move forward with needs to be thoroughly accomplished at the highest level of quality. If we do not aspire to this maximum level, we will always doubt our own sincerity and inevitably lose trust in ourselves.

   To accept yourself, you must fully pursue your purpose. Once you have accomplished the important task of living honestly by fulfilling honest actions, you can effectively share yourself with others. Most often we head out half-cocked and unprepared. Communicating and relating shallowly perpetuates the overwhelming confusion that prevails in the human condition and does not serve you or others well. It is time that you re-capture the spark of self-confidence and become a positive contributor to the necessary transformation of our species.

2. BECOME: This powerful self-directive allows you to release your self-imposed limitations creating the boundless person that you want to be. Most of us once had big dreams and aspirations. Somehow, we allowed them to slip away and be replaced by mundane and wasteful activities. In most cases, we substitute these dreams with the excuse,

"It is not realistic for me to attempt such a bold move." Children show us through their enthusiastic actions, that dreams can come true. It is our hope, that young children who grow into adults, never relinquish their excitement.

To become is the full circle of life. It has a starting and finishing point that cannot be distinguished, but is round, complete and with perfect form. It also can roll efficiently and move from place to place without concern. Embrace yourself and erase the roadblocks to your effectiveness. Only you have the power to become.

3. COMPASSION: Of all the emotions, there is no greater than compassion which is born out of pure love. This feeling emanates from the heart and is fully experienced when we permit ourselves to accept and become. This exuberance clearly frames the most important aspects of our being. With the never-ending race forward, it is healing to pause and reflect upon the power and relevance of the heart. The people who have left behind their greatest legacies are those with the utmost capacity for compassion. Do not think that this is an obscure and special gift. It is constantly available and waiting for you to use.

When we relax and permit a little bit of humility, our natural senses lead us into the center of this liberation. There is never a time that we should not employ compassionate action. All that we do in any endeavor needs to be wrapped with this provocative human asset.

4. DREAM: Our brain, the springboard to the mind, harbors extraordinary ability to create desired imagery. When pure thought is the kindling wood to ignite passion, we create artistic masterpieces. In simple terms, what we put in, we get

out. Sadly, as we mature, we are discouraged from dreaming and told that it is a youthful pursuit. Perceived reality displaces imagination and, before you know it, you place yourself in a pigeonhole that is uncomfortable and eventually destructive. Without the freedom of fantasy, we squelch the essence of our life. It has been and always will be the big dreamers who lead us forward toward the sun. Each and every time that you place energy in mental gymnastics, you will be rewarded. It is wondrous to consider that when we hear words, experience environments, or even employ our senses, pictorial images are conjured in the mind.

This is godliness at its best. From this starting point, we can paint a landscape that is so vivid, inviting and rewarding, that we will surely rest in the grace of such accomplishments. Music, similar to the orchestra of life, can roll forward, like a steam locomotive going up and down from the highest mountain to the deepest valley. This multi-sensual experience can place the audience into a dreamlike state, where your heart and imagination are truly the master composers of life – just enjoy.

5. EXERCISE: This utilitarian word is really a plethora of possibilities. It should not be looked at as an effort, but rather a harmonizer. Humans historically walked on the earth, ran up the hills, moved rocks, and stretched for the highest point. It has been only in the last few generations that we diminished the development of our bodies, with our sedentary lifestyles and habits. If we do not move, but stay in one position for too long, our anatomy literally begins to decompose. "Use it or lose it" is more profound than you know. As a matter of fact, most of us should be happy for gravity, because it is the only force that causes most of our bodies to maintain any level of homeostasis.

Every one of our cells depends upon ongoing aerobic movement (blood flow, oxygen, detoxification and increased temperature). In addition, the muscular skeletal structure requires resistant exercise that assures the density of hard tissue, (bones) and the shape, size and strength of muscle. The elongation of ligaments, cartilage, muscle tissue, etc. depends upon gentle stretch and flexibility. This trio of body sculpting requirements not only creates a healthy and functional anatomy, but also offers the mind and spirit a proper residence. Ongoing validation by observing people in the process of recovery and athleticism, led us to reveal that consistent exercise broadens mentality and inspires deep and complete spiritual possibilities. One cannot achieve good health without applying this vigorous threesome.

6. FUNCTION: This word has dual meanings. First, it can be stated that all purposeful acts must have a function. Second, the term can mean a gathering of individuals assembled for a purpose. Borrowing from both, you can unlock the power to better your daily life. When pursuing something, ask yourself what is the function of doing so. Will it help you create a worthy goal? Is it required to achieve something with great purpose? Sadly, it may also be something that leads you off track, drains your energy, or skews the issue. Obviously, in that case, you should not proceed. On the other hand, you may create a function that does not have to be limited to a gathering of people. It could be the destination you are attempting to reach, and where you finally tie all the ribbons that are leading your unified greatness.

You should always demand deep consciousness and focus before proceeding with anything you do. This contemplative time permits you to build an emotional and spiritual consensus, allowing your decision-making process to be conducted with grace and success. We must function at the highest level to fulfill our greatest purpose and passionately share that with all other life.

7. GODLINESS: In our ritualistic spiritual quests, we somehow have found a way to place a wedge between God and self. This clearly occurred when leaders in the majority of religions used hierarchical methods to convince the masses that they had to come to them to speak to God. Women, of course, were presented with a greater burden, since these devious dogmatists were men with an unfortunate view of females. All the brilliant theological writings clearly state that we are made in the image of God, and this God is not a dictatorial entity attempting to make life difficult at every turn.

Our lives should be lived to the fullest, most complete and integral manner. We should never hesitate to do our best. One should question their own sanity if they are involved with anything that they do when not engaging 100 percent of themselves. The reason most people are utterly miserable, is that they robotically move from action to action without even minimal awareness of what they are doing. As so well stated by Gandhi, "Be the change you want to see in the world." The laws of basic physics share the same time and space as the greatest spiritual environments.

Today you have the opportunity to break the shackles of narrow perception and embrace the endless potential of health and happiness. All struggle is manufactured by self-doubt and it is your obligation to uncover the darkest and most corrupt aspects that hold you back. As difficult as it is, you should be willing to face yourself daily with these seven components, and ask, "Am I achieving the Keys: Acceptance,

Become, Compassion, Dream, Exercise, Function, and Godliness?" These vivid guidelines will elevate you to live at the highest human level. This humanity is an exceptional gift that creates relevance and most important, significance. We need to practice being our best.

Once we are our best, we can share ourselves with others to achieve a healthy and happy life. Though self-discovery, all rewards of life will be available for you to beome peaceful. Truth is the fuel to keep the flame lit.

Humanity has failed to such a degree that most likely eight out of ten people live today in the past. It is like driving a car, yet turning around and looking at the back window as you speed ahead. Inevitably it is a grand way to sabotage a life worth living. A life that not only could enrich you as an individual, but all those that you touch. Consider as a mother or father or even as a supervisor where you are now, directly affecting others. While you are willing to embrace long ago, remember where you are right now. All too often I hear people state, "If it could only be like it used to be." "Used to be" is an illusion and the only thing that brings joy is this very moment. Begin to respect the present.

To harvest happiness out of current events requires an unwavering commitment to fulfilling your values. Many people reading this may have some vague concept of what that means yet value-driven lives are the lives that positively impact our species. This existence is not about survival it's about sharing, giving, trusting, loving and supporting. There is nothing else more important for us to do than to cultivate these acts of kindness that not only fulfill your own need for peace and harmony, but also assist all others in achieving theirs. *Discovering YOU in You* will help you in all aspects of your life.

INTEGRITY   *POWER*

"Everything we hear is an opinion, not a fact. Everything we see is a perspective, not the truth...He who lives in harmony with himself lives in harmony with the universe...Receive without conceit, and release without struggle...be content to see what you really are... The universe is changing; our life is what our thoughts make it."
                                             ᥫᩣ **Marcus Aurelius**

*D*iscovering *YOU in You* presents the knowledge and expertise conveyed by the authors and their colleagues at Hippocrates. We aspire our readers find their own happiness and healing paths, using the themes and information presented to create their personalized roadmap for celebrating their lives. Our vision is that each person discovers themselves to contribute to the greater good of all. Health and Happiness can only be found within you; healing takes place when you have a strong sense of self, then joy and love follows. The self gets stronger with practice.

These powerful themes are the foundation of a successful self-discovery journey:

HEALTH (food, exercise, stress free lifestyle, and wellness)

HAPPINESS (joy, self-actualization, fulfillment, bliss, and peace)

INTERACTIONS (connections, sharing, communication, and listening)

Self-competence and self-discovery evolve from awareness of strengths and limitations. This is a changeable perception that can be altered via the expansion of our potential. Primal man not only survived but thrived with instinct, which is the cradle of trust. As we "evolve" our energy migrates to the field of cerebral engagement and the intellectual entrapments of modern humanity. We need to learn who we are for a peaceful life to accept inherent knowledge.

Discovery is an unexpected gift that opens your life to the authentic self that you have always been. Self-realization is the acceptance of the newly discovered whole person that is now capable of manifesting any and all dreams. You are the YOU in you. Create the future, NOT an excuse. Finding your inherent truth will help discover your inherent power.

Consciousness and a Confident Self

Consciousness keeps us aware, cognoscente, and heart centered. Confidence inspires trust.

Reassembling trust is a matter of embracing the voice that resonates inside. All too often we attempt to draw our confidence from the trust that others place in us. This is like waiting for a ride that never comes. Become the sculpture that manifests the image of uncompromising clarity. Once we acknowledge our commitment to life's purpose, our integrated self will assemble like an artist's creation. This work is born from creative energy and imagination.

We are made of energy and vibration which emanate from us connecting to the infinite universe. Interconnectedness is inevitable and there is no person or place where we do not interchange. Our own fountain of energy flows from self-acceptance, a humble heart, and the openness of a child. Provoking consciousness guides us into every experience. What results is a healthy, happy and creative life that is abundant with perpetual joy and extraordinary potential. Creativity is manifested from trust, belief, and bravery.

The road to happiness involves letting go of old habits and beliefs that have kept us from spiritually being prosperous, and content. The journey to health and happiness requires being whole, honest, and loyal. Once the realization of who you are, and who you really want to be, comes into focus you must take immediate action to make the necessary changes to manifest reality. Discovering YOU in You enables your instinct to liberate true happiness. Your emotions block you; therefore, they need to be pure, honest, and expressive.

The emotional self has no verbal language; however, it can express itself via the spirit through stillness and intuition. Revealing feelings is a musical, rhythmic matter, and assembles the soundtrack for an invigorated life. Self-confidence exudes a refined persona, emotional intelligence, clear knowledge and a sense of accomplishment. One of the side effects of such earth changing results is joy. Bliss is being in control of our emotions, and accepting knowledge with self-assurance and confidence. Ultimately, it is your objective to submerse and bathe your sorrows away. This ignites a joyous orchestration manifesting a beautiful and untainted existence. The need for belief and trust in self will support your freedom from disease.

HAPPINESS

Peace and Bliss

True happiness depends on maintaining healthy relationships and non-toxic social interactions. All people in relationships must be on the same page. They can share similar, as well as different interests. People do not require identical companions; however, they need to participate in mutual activities. Without comradery we drift apart. This involves authentic and honest communication. Bliss is achieved when self-realization and joy have evolved to shared interactions. Above all, do not lose peaceful thoughts since fear and anger are always looming nearby.

Pam Blue, M.Ed., was the director of education, and guided the course which is now the Hippocrates Mastery Program. Pam succinctly presented her views on health, happiness, and interactions:

> Our health is manifested by doing the work. It is something that requires daily maintenance and attention to high vibration nutrition. This nutrition can come in many forms. It may be a raw vegan, sprout-based diet, or it may be a deeper level of self-awareness and reflection. It may be a greater alignment physiologically or a change in our life choices, decisions and actions. All in all, health is an inclusive concept which is discovered and expressed uniquely. It calls us to connect intimately with our potential and to finally realize the impact we have upon one another and our environment. It is our responsibility to harmonize the two.
>
> Our happiness is in direct relationship to our health. As we discover our power to choose our beliefs and our mindsets, we unleash the ability to live consciously every moment. This in and of itself naturally gives us the experience of happiness. It is the result of being whole and complete; by merging the mind, body and spirit into the space and time we are given. Thus, happiness is recognition of the power within ourselves and the moments we experience. Developing and refining our perception is our creative way of expanding happiness and joy. Our perceptions can support our well-being and optimal self-confidence.
>
> Our interactions are a consistent barometer for our wellness. We are constantly relating whether it be to ourselves, one another, or our environment. These opportunities to connect provide a backdrop for us to experience our inner work, and subsequently, the level of our well-being. Looking at the body as a measure, we witness cells relating to other cells, and organs relating to other organs. We recognize that a healthy realized person considers the bigger picture, and the greater good of something beyond self. Thus, the bridge of peaceful communication is a core consideration in the conquest of health.

Good health is an indication that we have balanced the different parts of self. As we become self-realized while interacting with others, we become the best we can be which leads to happiness. When we are truly the best we can be and share ourselves in reciprocal relationships, we achieve bliss. Social interactions require awareness, honesty, and open dialogue to promote intimacy. Keeping the best of ourselves alive makes self-discovery easy and our experience joyful.

INTERACTIONS

Love and Intimacy

Over time, we have counseled tens of thousands in Europe and North America, and one common theme revealed, was that physical and emotional disorders create a lack of intimacy. Our knowledge on this subject comes not only from the endless learning acquired during health consultations, but also from our own encounters as parents, grandparents and fellow humans. It is important to have a positive mindset, exercise, and to eat well; it is even more important to recognize our sexuality. It's important to become comfortable with it, and utilize its every nuance in a proper, positive way to gain the spectacular advantages that it affords.

Our ultimate desire is that these words will impel you enough to liberate you, a beautiful, giving person deep and soulful. Once the force of nature is energized, your life's purpose will be revealed. We have also observed hundreds of individuals who found authentic love and shared themselves in a healthy way via intimacy. This loving act often manifests into healing energy and heightened wellness. We have approached sexual vitality with a comprehensive view.

Ken Blue and Pam Fisher met at HHI over ten years ago, and were married shortly thereafter. As our chef and director of education, Ken and Pam, ignited their love on the campus of Hippocrates. Ken's original romance was with the cuisine he beautifully creates on a daily basis. His sensitivity to the texture, fragrance, and rainbow colors from the garden's bounty make him uniquely positioned as one of the world's leading plant based chefs. Pam is as maternal as mother earth. Possessing a wisdom of history and knowledge. Her heightened and refined senses uniquely elevate her as a facilitator of depth and understanding. Together their bond has emulsified their hearts into one. Supporting one another and all those they touch empowers the ether via their pure devotion.

The warm and sunny day for their wedding ceremony at the Institute's Grass Hut is one of the fondest events ever held. Like two freshly cut flowers, they united to become a magnificent bouquet. Following the ceremony, all who attended sat in awe of them gracefully navigating the room with tai chi and qigong stances in unison. This very moment revealed the evidence of this palatable partnership. Years later, they have matured in their commitment with an endless flow of energy and compassion exuding from their bond.

When sharing intimacy with the person that we truly love, it is a spiritual and enriching gift. When one considers intimacy and sexuality as a spiritual event, there is a complete change in attitude about this holy act. Sharing love fosters the highest level of consciousness. Love itself is the essence of creative power. By applying this force, one sparks the connectivity between us and the endless universe. Love is all around us and when we connect with nature, we are complete.

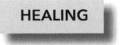

HEALING

Health and Well-Being

Your needs are physical, as well as emotional, and require mental and intellectual stimulation. The five senses (hearing, seeing, touching, tasting and smelling) comprise your basic physical needs. This includes sleep, safety, and any other physical requirement like oxygen, water, or food. Health follows when you are aware of what's missing and resolve to find it. Your emotional well-being requires constant attention. You are in charge of yourself and only you can find what works best for you. The job of self-discovery is yours alone.

This is work that requires dedication, diligence, and commitment. Once you organize all the health and wellness input coming into your brain that pertains to you, then you will pick and choose what is best. Identify what you need to create health and well-being formula. This will help balance and evaluate you. Put what you've learned into daily practice. One way to do this is through Qigong, an ancient Chinese system of physical exercise and breathing. Ultimate health and well-being is your priority.

Brian and Anna Maria are a great example of trust and respect in a long-term partnership. The best relationships are when we can be our authentic selves and flourish into the best we can be. The partnership between Brian and Anna Maria is successful because they share their love and expertise with each one of us. Their strength comes from all the adversity they've faced and have overcome together. They are always available for consultation and will never let us down with their unconditional care. They have mastered communication skills, as well as teaching others how to heal themselves through food and emotional well-being.

All too often, we tend to question our motives when we do not have a concise road map and clear goal in mind. When your focus is to live at a maximum level, your results are maximum. This proposition is necessary adding these directives to your already busy life, which is most likely daunting. There is no doubt that when you take the first step, your existence will transform into a happy and productive one. It is never a burden to work in the natural systems. Your reward will be greater clarity, diminished fear, and ultimately a fulfilling lifestyle that allows you to make meaningful and creative contributions.

Everyone is responsible for learning what they need to become healthy and happy. Being open to creative ideas will assist in understanding yourself. George Bernard Shaw said: "Imagination is the beginning of creation. You imagine what you desire; you will what you imagine, and at last you exude what you will." We have the gift to imagine and create every day and it is up to us to expand our purpose. Our work to reach our goals includes building our own personal formula.

Building Your Happiness Formula

There are four supportive columns to guide the completion of your formula. Each column is a practice that guides you to understand yourself. You achieve new levels with each column:

1. Immunity – protection from infection
2. Confidence – courage and truth
3. Gratitude – thankfulness and kindness
4. New You – acceptance and commitment

These guides will help you on your wellness path and are ongoing throughout life. As Marcus Aurelius said two thousand years ago, *"When jarred unavoidably by circumstances, revert at once to yourself, and do not lose the rhythm more than you can help. You will have a better grasp of harmony if you keep going back to it."* Discovering the "New You" is a lifetime adventure filled with changes, discovery, learning, and exploration. Going back to yourself is key.

The joy of birthing a health and happiness formula takes commitment and observation to make proper choices, such as nourishment which fuels emotional levity. Everyone is different, so each body has unique requirements. Do not rely on outside forces, but be your own master for what is best. Your goal is to find sustenance, interests, and projects that enrich.

The formula for achieving bliss is by becoming an individual who is self-realized and self-actualized. You are now able to engage in successful interactions with others to procure joy. Our task is to keep ourselves healthy and calm so that we can share our innermost joyous selves. Laughter and enjoyment are by-products of living a blissful existence. Laughter gives us relief from stress and anxiety.

Health and happiness go together. Money can't buy you happiness, only your own attitudes and behaviors can change living a life full of sadness or pain. As the Roman Emperor of the second century said in his book called "Meditations": *"Look well into thyself; there is a source of strength which will always spring up if thou wilt always look"*. Memories are there and you can choose which ones to keep and which to discard. Pick those that help you construct your personal happiness journey.

Principles for building your formula:

1. Know your life and purpose. Know your environment and those beings that care for you sincerely and authentically.

2. Know your needs and how to satiate them. Understand what is absolute and know what you cannot live without.

3. Know your diet and what gives you energy or what makes you sluggish. Eat foods that nourish you.

4. Know how to balance your emotions. Manage your thoughts so you can determine their resulting effect.

5. Know who you are; believe in your true self; trust yourself. You need to feel satisfied with who you are to be happy.

Bliss is the pinnacle for happiness which occurs when you connect with your inner voice and embrace the magnificent world. Meditation and breath are proven techniques, since they force awareness. Where you are, and how to be in the present moment is determined by heart driven guidance. The breath is the bridge between body and thought. These historic techniques require self-discipline, and pure acceptance of all events in every situation.

You will find what is necessary to balance yourself – the way to live – as Marcus Aurelius (a philosophical genius and poignant guide who ruled the Roman Empire 161-180 AD) said: *"Never let the future disturb you. You will meet it, if you have to, with the same weapons of reason which today arm you against the present."* He continues with more knowledge from his book Meditations, *"You have the power over your mind – not outside events. Realize this, and you will find strength."* And finally, *"Our life is what our thoughts make it....Very little is needed to make a happy life; it is all within yourself, in your way of thinking."* Trust and listen to yourself to achieve your goals.

You have to know what fulfills you. Be confident and acknowledge your needs. Awareness, trust, and honesty spark the process of constructing your formula. You can do this with instinctual knowledge, and abundant openness to forge your path to healing. We will guide you in your journey. Interpersonal relationships should always be molded around loving companions who share the desire to expand their joy factor. Healing occurs with loving energy, and healing power is within each of us.

CONCLUSION

Compassion and mutual sharing will add a feeling of belonging. Happiness exists and when we choose to accept and bathe in it, love can then be a harmonious key. Joy is wonderful when we share who we are with others. Bliss is the highest level of happiness and can easily occur with someone or with groups. It is with passion that one moves forward vigorously to achieve the enriched heart. Historically, contemplation, prayer, and meditation have all been instrumental in achieving this. Keep joy in your heart.

Healing begins when you discover YOU in you. Never give up; find the courage to persevere. Trust your intuitive feelings. Ask yourself these questions: "Do I know what really makes me happy? What is my personal formula for joy? How do I prepare myself for ultimate bliss? How do I maintain my happiness level"? You must respond with your own ideas in order to create your own personal equation. Joy and happiness in your life will help you find your own formula and the strategy that works best for you. To keep and maintain your desired happiness level, constant awareness and meditation are required. Healing will occur naturally. Practice healing habits for ultimate happiness.

We thoroughly enjoyed writing this book, Discovering YOU in You which reflects our passion, practices, experiences, and hope for all future generations. We are open to questions, comments, or new ideas to continue our mission. The goal of Discovering YOU in You is to help you find your personal peace, your higher spiritual self, and to guide you in living a fulfilling and purposeful life. To love and be loved authentically is what we yearn for. To accomplish these goals you must do the work required within and understand your interactions in addition to living a healthy life. Your choices and thoughts depict your personal level of happiness. Honesty and truth guarantee your success.

Life is like dance. Once you learn and practice the right steps for you, you will live an exhilarated and joyous life to share with loved ones. Thank you for spending time with us exploring the realms of human potential at its finest. We wish you a healthy, happy, and long life. Purity and truth guarantee your success. Without reality healing can be thwarted. Be open and honest. Enjoy life.

Brian Clement, Ph.D., NMD, LN

Dr. Brian Clement, PhD, NMD, L.N. has spearheaded the internationally progressive Lifestyle Medicine movement for more than five decades. He is the director of the renowned Hippocrates Health Institute in West Palm Beach, Florida (U.S.A.), the world's foremost complementary residential Lifestyle Medicine Health Mecca. Over the last half century he and his team have pioneered clinical research and training in disease prevention and helped hundreds of thousands of participants who provided volumes of data, giving Clement a privileged insight into the lifestyle required to avert disease, enhance longevity, and maintain vitality. These findings have provided the basis for Hippocrates progressive, state-of-the-art treatments and programs for health and recovery – forging the way to the creation of their signature program, the Life Transformation Program.

Brian Clement has written over twenty books focused on health, spirituality, and natural healing. Among them are *Living Foods for Optimum Health, Longevity,* and *LifeForce*, which Dr. Colin Campbell calls "One of the most important books ever written on nutrition. *Supplements Exposed*, reveals the pharmaceutical fraud rampant in the sales, production, and distribution of worthless and even harmful vitamin pills.

Additionally, he has authored three volumes for the scientific community Food is Medicine. One of his most popular books, *7 Keys to Lifelong Sexual Vitality*, is touted as an important guide to the biology of love. *Dairy Deception* spotlights the hazards with the consumption of dairy, eggs and their offspring and *Sweet Disease* exposes the perils and detrimental impact consuming sugar has on the human body. His latest works, such as, *MANopause,* which is now available, while *Quantum Human Biology* and *Natural Weight Loss* will be published soon.

Brian Clement is a devoted husband and a caring father of four, who along with his wife, Anna Maria Gahns-Clement Ph.D., L.N., co-directs the Hippocrates Health Institute. In addition to his research studies, Clement conducts conferences and lectures worldwide on attaining health and creating longevity, giving humanity a roadmap for redirecting, enriching and extending their lives. A licensed nutritionist, Brian Clement is a graduate of the University of Science, Arts, and Technology where he earned his Ph.D. Brian's dedication to teaching health and happiness is unprecedented.

Katherine C. Powell, Ed.D.

Katherine Copsinis Powell is an accomplished educator, author, researcher, and computer pioneer. As a full time instructor and adjunct professor at Florida Atlantic University (FAU), she has helped thousands of students find their true callings, giving them the tools and knowledge to become great teachers. After graduating college, Katherine entered the corporate world and became a high-level executive, entrepreneur, and business consultant in computers. She also spent three years teaching and consulting in St. Thomas, U.S. Virgin Islands. She has shared her truth and expertise with audiences all over the world. She has travelled over twenty times to Europe and five times to South America.

Katherine has authored seven books: one was on the glass ceiling (*Confidence and Coping Skills for Executive Women*), two textbooks were on educational psychology of the self, and one was a textbook (co-authored) on creative literacy for young children. She graduated from HHI's Health Educator Program (HED). She also co-wrote the *Belief* book with Brian Clement and *The Power of a Woman*, with Anna Maria Clement. Dr. Powell has devoted her life to research on self-confidence, self-awareness, cognitive development, and becoming the best you can be. Her greatest joy is seeing others reach their highest level and full potential.

Katherine has published over fifty articles and presented her work in forums at Oxford University, in England, and Athens University, in Greece. She also has conducted several workshops in the United States. Katherine has a Bachelor of Arts (BA) in Bio-Chemistry, from Syracuse University; a Master of Arts (MA) in Social Sciences (Creative Psychology), from Boston College, and a Doctor in Education (Ed.D) in human development from UMASS, at Amherst, MA.

She was a professor in Educational Psychology, an entrepreneur in business, and a computer data-base designer, implementing banking systems with teams of over eighty people. Katherine is known for her ability to complete projects successfully and her extensive travels have given her insightful experiences to help others. She has devoted her life to helping thousands of students and employees in becoming the best they can be, such as developing confidence, courage, discipline, and perseverance. All dreams can be fulfilled with intent, hard work, practice, and never giving up on your goals. Dr. Powell believes that everyone can reach the best they can be through self-motivation, belief, and self-discipline.

REFERENCES

Amen, D. Healing. *ADD: The Break Through Program That Allows You to See the 6 Types of ADD.* Penguin Group, New York, 2001.

Bandura, A. *Social Foundations of Thought and Action: A Social Cognitive Theory.* Prentice Hall, Englewood Cliffs, NJ, 1986.

Bandura, A. *Self-Efficacy: The Exercise of Control.* W.H. Freeman, New York, NY, 1997.

Carson, R. *The Sea Around Us.* Oxford University Press, New York, NY, 1951.

Chopra, D. & Tanzi R. *Super Brain: Unleashing the Explosive Power of Your Mind to Maximize Health, Happiness and Spiritual Well-Being.* Harmony Books, New York, NY, 2013.

Cooper, J.C. Taoism. *The Way of the Mystic.* Harper Collins, New York, NY, 1990.

Clement, A.M. *A Families Guide to Health & Healing.* Hippocrates Publishing, West Palm Beach, FLA, 2005.

Clement, A.M. & Clement, B.R. *Killer Clothes.* Book Pub Co. Summertown, TN, 2011.

Clement, B.R. & Clement A. M. *7 Keys to Lifelong Sexual Vitality.* New World Library, Novato, CA, 2012.

Clement, B. R. *Sweet Disease.* Hippocrates Health Institute, West Palm Beach, FLA, 2015.

Clement, B. R. *Poison Poultry.* Hippocrates Health Institute, West Palm Beach, FLA, 2017.

Clement, B. R. *Longevity.* Jouvence, Las Vegas, NV, 2006.

Clement, B. R. *Supplements Exposed.* New Page Books, Newburyport, MA, 2009.

Clement, B.R. & Powell, K, C. *Belief: Integrity in Relationships.* Hippocrates Health Institute, west Palm Beach, FLA, 2013.

Clement, B.R. *Emospirit.* Hippocrates Health Institute, west Palm Beach, FLA, 2016.

Clement, B.R. *Life Force: Superior Health and Longevity.* Healthy Living Pub. Summertown, TN, 2007.

Clement, B.R. *Killer Fish.* Book Pub Co., Summertown, TN, 2012.

Clement, B.R. *Dairy Deception.* Hippocrates Health Institute, West Palm Beach, FLA, 2014.

Clement B.R. *Living Foods for Optimum Health.* Three River

Press, New York, NY, 1996.

Clement, A.M. & Powell, K.C. *The Power of a Woman*. Hippocrates Health Institute, West Palm Beach, FLA, 2014.

Clement, A.M. *Healthy Cuisine*. Book Pub Co, 2008.

Clement, B.R. & Clement, A.M. *MANopause*. Rowman& Littlefield, Carnham, MD, 2020.

Clement, B.R. *Food Vol I, II, III*. Hippocrates Health Institute, West Palm Beach, FLA, 2015.

Clinton, H. *It Takes a Village*. Simon & Schuster, New York, NY, 2006.

Cloud, H. & Townsend., J. Boundaries: *When to Say Yes, How to Say No to Take Control of Your Life*. Zondervan, Grand Rapids, MI, 1992.

Connell, R. *Gender*. Polity Press, Oxford, UK, 2002.

Craig, G.I. *Human Development: An Integrated Study of Life Span*. Prentice Hall, Upper Saddle River, NJ, 1994.

De Beauvoir, S. *The Second Sex*. Knopf Doubleday Pub Group, New York, NY, 1949.

Durant, W. *The Story of Philosophy: The Lives and Opinions of the*

Greater Philosophers. Washington Square Press, New York, NY, 1961.

Powell, K.C. *Educational Psychology of the Self: An Inter-Active Workbook.* Kendall Hunt, Dubuque, IA, 2006.

Powell. K. C. *Educational Psychology of the Self and Learning.* Pearson, Boston, MA, 2012.

Randolph, C.W. & James, G. *From Hormone Hell to Hormone Well.* Health Communications, Inc. Deerfield Beach, FLA. 2009.

Roman, Andy B. *Deep Feeling Deep Healing The Heart Mind and Soul of Getting Well.* Spectrum Healing Press, Jupiter, FLA, 2001.

Sandberg, S. *Lean In: Women, Work and the Will to Lead.* Knopf Double Day Pub Group, New York, NY, 2013.

Santrock, J.w. *Educational Psychology.* McGraw Hill, Boston MA, 2012.

Shoknoff, J.P. *Protecting Brains. Not Simply Stimulating Minds.* Science. 333(6045), pp. 982-983, 2011.

Skinner, B. F. *About Behaviorism.* Alfred A. Knopf, New York, NY, 1974.

Slavin, R.E. *Cooperative Learning: Theory, Research and Practice.* Allyn& Bacon, Boston, MA, 1995.

Spar, D.L. *Wonder Woman: Sex Power and the Conquest for Perfection*. Sarah Crichton Books, New York, NY, 2014.

Stein, N. *Jung's Map of the Soul: An Introduction*. Open Court Publishing, Chicago, IL, 1998.

Steinberg, R. *Metaphors of Mind, Conceptions of the Nature of Intelligence*. Cambridge University Press, New York, NY, 1990.

Storr, A. *The Essential Jung*. MIF Books, New York, NY, 1983.

Tannen, D. *Gender and Discourse*. Oxford University Press, New York, NY. 1994.

Tannen, D. *Talking from 9 to 5*. William Morrow & Co, New York, NY, 1994.

Tyson, P. & Tyson R.M. *Psychoanalytic Theories of Development: An Integration*. Yale University Press, New Haven CT, 2009.

Vaknin, S. *Malignant Self Love Narcissism Revisited*. A Narcissus Publications, Skopje Macedonia, 2003.

Vygotsky, D. & Christie, J. *Thought and Language*. MIT Press, Cambridge, MA, 2009.

Warren, E. *A Fighting Chance*. Metropolitan Books, New York, NY 2014.

Welstead, S. *Searching for You: Ideas About Healthy Relationships.* Volumes Pub, Canada, 2009.

Wheatley, M. *Turning to One Another: Simple Conversations to Restore Hope in the Future.* Berrett-Koehler Publishers, San Francicso, CA, 2002.

Wollstonecraft, M.A. *A Vindications of the Rights of Women.* Courier Dover Pub, Mineola, NY, 1792.'

Woolfolk, A. *Educational Psychology.* Allyn& Bacon, Boston, MA, 2001.

Wikipedia & Google provided URLs for name, dates, and other information.